but I've fou... ...at appeals to
me even mo... ...paused, then continued
with businesslike crispness, "Spend a weekend
with me and I'll settle for two seats on the
board and an audit. In return, I won't take
any further action for twelve months."

Caroline was absolutely livid. What did he
take her for? A piece of high-class
merchandise that he could purchase at whim?

"Get out of here! I'd die before I'd let you
touch me."

"That comment is going to cost you, Carrie.
When you change your mind—and you
will—you can come to my office and ask me
very nicely if the offer is still good."

BROOKE HASTINGS
is an avid reader who loves to travel. She draws
her material from many sources: the newspaper, politics, the places she visits and the people
she meets. Her unique plots, full of real people
who meet love in many guises, make her one of
the best new writers in this field.

Dear Reader:

At Silhouette we try to publish books with you, our reader, in mind, and we're always trying to think of something new. We're very pleased to announce the creation of Silhouette First Love, a new line of contemporary romances written by the very finest young adult writers especially for our twelve-to-sixteen-year-old readers. First Love has many of the same elements you've enjoyed in Silhouette Romances—love stories, happy endings and the same attention to detail and description—but features heroines and situations with which our younger readers can more easily identify.

First Love from Silhouette will be available in bookstores this October. We will introduce First Love with six books, and each month thereafter we'll bring you two new First Love romances.

We welcome any suggestions or comments, and I invite you to write to us at the address below.

Karen Solem
Editor-in-Chief
Silhouette Books
P.O. Box 769
New York, N.Y. 10019

BROOKE HASTINGS
Winner Take All

Silhouette Romance

Published by Silhouette Books New York

America's Publisher of Contemporary Romance

Other Silhouette Romances by Brooke Hastings

Playing for Keeps   *Desert Fire*
Innocent Fire   *Island Conquest*

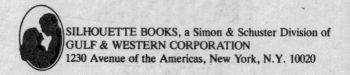

SILHOUETTE BOOKS, a Simon & Schuster Division of
GULF & WESTERN CORPORATION
1230 Avenue of the Americas, New York, N.Y. 10020

Copyright © 1981 by Brooke Hastings

Distributed by Pocket Books

All rights reserved, including the right to reproduce
this book or portions thereof in any form whatsoever.
For information address Silhouette Books, 1230
Avenue of the Americas, New York, N.Y. 10020

ISBN: 0-671-57102-8

First Silhouette printing September, 1981

10 9 8 7 6 5 4 3 2 1

All of the characters in this book are fictitious. Any resemblance to actual persons, living or dead, is purely coincidental.

Map by Tony Ferrara

SILHOUETTE, SILHOUETTE ROMANCE and colophon are
trademarks of Simon & Schuster.

America's Publisher of Contemporary Romance

Printed in the U.S.A.

*For Alan and Bruce
and, especially,
Marilyn*

Winner
Take All

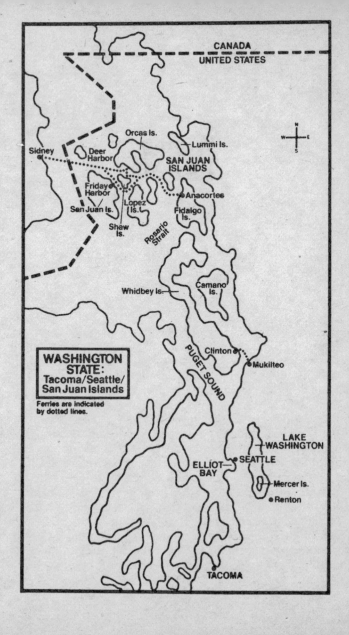

Chapter One

Caroline McKay Spencer had been president and chairman of the board of Elliot Bay Electronics Corporation for just over a year now. Surely, she thought to herself on a dreary January Tuesday, she should be accustomed to the fact that the firm's longtime controller, Sam Hanover, always made a point of walking down the hall to *her* office whenever he wanted to speak with her. But Sam had been both teacher and guide during the thirteen months since her husband's death, and Caroline invariably felt inexperienced by comparison.

She sometimes wished that Sam had accepted the presidency of the corporation rather than persuaded the board that the position rightfully belonged to her. Certainly he had been the more qualified candidate, despite the late Clay Spencer's relentless insistence that she prepare herself for the top slot. She owed a great deal to the wily Sam Hanover—she never could have fulfilled her duties as president so competently without his encouragement and advice.

Over the years Caroline had learned that it was wisest to conceal her real emotions from others. She had known Sam since her childhood, however, and although she was reserved with him, she was not as aloof as with most of her employees. As they sat together in her spacious office, she looked at him across the old leather and maple desk she had inherited from Clay. Sam was a stocky man in his sixties, his sparse gray hair combed across his bald head, his blue eyes wintry.

"The expression on your face is as cold as our Seattle weather today, Sam," Caroline remarked lightly. "What's wrong?"

"I had a call last night from Adam." The words were clipped off and flung out, Sam's curt tone reminding Caroline of the way Clay had always sounded whenever he was forced to utter the name of his older brother, Adam Spencer. Long ago the two men had been partners, founding Elliot Bay Electronics on the sound basis of Clay's background in electronic engineering and Adam's ability as a business administrator. Clay had been a virtual wizard when it came to the world of semiconductor technology and very high speed integrated circuits. Under his leadership the company had developed and manufactured complex navigational equipment for boats, planes, and mass transit systems, producing a comfortable living for both brothers.

But when the firm was only four years old, they had quarreled bitterly about the terms of their father's will. In the end, Adam had sold half of his stock to Caroline's late father, Alex McKay, and moved to southern California to join a larger company. Alex then took over the administration of the firm, which once again freed Clay to continue with his beloved research. He was fascinated by the field of electronic warfare, with its monitoring and surveillance devices and sensitive radar equipment. Eventually he invented a jamming system that could be installed on ships, missiles, and planes to make them invisible to enemy radar. The result was a number of lucrative contracts, both with the government and with weapons manufacturers.

Adam Spencer still owned nine percent of the now thriving corporation; Caroline was the largest shareholder, having inherited stock from both her father and her late husband. But Elliot Bay Electronics—or EBE, as everyone called the firm—was now a publicly owned corporation, its stock traded on the over-the-counter exchange, so there were many minor shareholders as well. Like all public companies, it was subject to a whole array of government laws and regulations.

Caroline turned away from the past and back to Sam. Her face registered no reaction to his announcement, even though she was curious about the reason for Adam's call. They had last heard from him when Clay died.

"He informed me that he had arranged to sell his shares in the company to Matthew Lyle," Sam continued, an angry frown on his thin lips. "The transaction takes place this morning. Nice of him to give us advance notice, wasn't it?"

Caroline had never heard Sam sound so bitingly sarcastic. "Matthew Lyle?" she repeated, not hiding her genuine puzzlement at this piece of news. "What would he want with us?"

"Why does some nut decide to climb Mount Everest? Maybe just because we're *here*. The guy gets his kicks from taking over corporations that don't want to be acquired. He's been at it since he was twenty-five years old. In ten years he's added over a dozen companies to the Olympia Industries group, and at least half of them kicked and screamed every inch of the way."

The prospect of tangling with the very formidable Matthew Lyle was not at all appealing to Caroline, but she managed to sound utterly confident as she told Sam smoothly, "Nine percent might get him a seat on the board of directors, but it won't give him control of the firm. Projected earnings for next year are excellent, and the shareholders trust us. There's no reason to think they would vote to sell out to Matthew Lyle."

"Face facts, Carrie!" Sam Hanover said wearily. "You hold eighteen percent of the company. The other six members of the board—assuming we can count on them—own about twelve percent combined. Our stock is selling at nineteen dollars a share, when its real value is nearly thirty dollars. If Lyle is intent on a takeover, he'll propose that his own slate of directors be elected at the annual meeting in May. And he'll promise the stockholders that once he controls the board of directors the board will vote to liquidate the company's assets—sell everything on the open market. Who knows how much we'd bring on the auction block? Maybe as much as forty dollars per share. And most of the stockholders will take the profits and run. Lyle will use his share of the money to finance other investments."

"But he hasn't usually liquidated companies in the past," Caroline pointed out. She had followed Sam's explanation carefully, even though nothing in it was new to her. Though corporate finance was not her strongest point, she had learned a great deal over the last few years.

"That's true," Sam conceded. "If he's after EBE

itself rather than just cash from the sale of it, he'll probably promise the stockholders that if his slate of directors is elected Olympia Industries will acquire EBE. Our shareholders would receive Olympia stock in exchange for their current EBE stock. Lyle's company is a phenomenon, Carrie—especially given the present economy. Most of the shareholders will jump at the chance to own a piece of it."

"Maybe *most*," Caroline emphasized, "but surely not *all*. You just said we can probably depend on controlling the thirty percent of EBE stock owned by me and the rest of the board. Taking over a company isn't easy, and Matthew Lyle is starting with a big handicap. He has nine percent. He needs fifty-one percent. The annual meeting is only four months away, and that's not much time to get signed proxies from thousands of stockholders who've always supported *us*."

"I envy your optimism, considering the fact that a few hundred people together own seventy-five percent of our stock," Sam replied dourly. "Lyle will get to them, Carrie. Sometimes I think he won't be happy until he owns all of the Pacific Northwest. Shipping, shipbuilding, lumber, weapons systems, agriculture . . ." He sighed and then fixed his determined blue eyes on Caroline. The bald spot on his head glistened with perspiration. "I aim to fight him, Carrie. He's not getting his hands on Elliot Bay Electronics."

"Let's sit tight for a week or two, Sam," Caroline suggested. "We really don't know what Lyle has in mind, and it will give us a chance to find out. Now that he owns more than five percent of our stock, doesn't he have to report any further purchases to the Securities and Exchange Commission?"

Sam nodded. "That's right. Luckily for us, there isn't much that the S.E.C. doesn't regulate. At least we'll be able to keep track of what he's up to."

"Good. Let's keep this between the two of us for the time being, Sam. I'll talk informally with some of the major shareholders—call them up and feel them out to see if Lyle's been in contact with any of them. I think we can head off his power play before it ever gets started."

"It already *has* started, Carrie," Sam snapped out as he rose from his chair. "It's up to you to stop it!"

Caroline did not care for Sam's domineering order, but she kept her features bland and rose as well, taking his arm and giving it a gentle pat as they walked out the door of her office together. Her executive secretary, Maggie O'Connell, cocked an inquiring eyebrow at her as Sam walked briskly through the outer office into the hall. Caroline merely smiled and returned to work, not yet ready to confide anything to anyone—even Maggie.

She had never seen the usually poker-faced controller so agitated, she thought to herself as she doodled absent-mindedly on a blank piece of paper. Of course, he had spent twenty years of his working life with Elliot Bay Electronics and was nearing retirement age. She knew that he had a fierce emotional attachment to the company. No doubt he was afraid that if Matthew Lyle engineered a successful takeover Sam Hanover would be out of a job.

Before Clay's death Caroline had worked in the company's marketing department, and on one occasion her job had brought her into contact with Olympia Industries, the umbrella corporation that was controlled by Matthew Lyle. She was trying to sell Lyle Marine Construction a new navigational system intended for small pleasure craft, but EBE was underbid by a large, Boston-based firm. Caroline had had no dealings with Matthew Lyle himself. Although he was an avid yachtsman who had entered, and won, quite a few races and still had a special interest in Lyle Marine, the company founded by his father, most of his time was taken up in running and expanding the parent corporation, Olympia Industries.

From time to time, photographs of the dynamic Lyle had appeared in the business or sports sections of the Seattle and Tacoma papers. Frequently a beautiful woman was hanging on his arm, staring adoringly upward while he ignored her presence. He certainly looked the part of the ruthless, wealthy businessman—so much so that Caroline had once facetiously asked Maggie whether he might in fact be an actor, hired by Olympia Industries from some mysterious casting agency in Hollywood for the express purpose of intimidating the entire West Coast. He was never photographed with a smile on his face, and Caroline, although admitting that he was quite attractive, had mentally characterized him as a hard, unemotional man.

The news that he now owned nine percent of Elliot Bay Electronics was unpalatable indeed, and Caroline resolutely set about stopping any planned takeover before the man had time to do further damage. During the rest of the week she phoned many of the company's major stockholders, gingerly feeling out their positions and carefully hiding her dismay at the end of each conversation.

"He's certainly thorough," she remarked to Sam Hanover late on Friday afternoon. Her preliminary investigations had revealed two things. First, Matthew Lyle had been quietly purchasing EBE stock for almost a year, and now owned about three and a half percent in addition to the nine percent he had just acquired from Adam Spencer. There was also no doubt that he intended to buy more stock as it became available.

Second, either Lyle or his cousin and chief lieutenant Joseph Symington had spoken informally with most of the major stockholders weeks, or even months, ago. Lyle and Symington had subtly hinted at their belief that EBE was worth far more than the price of its stock would indicate. In one recent conversation Lyle had even mentioned a possible even exchange of EBE stock for Olympia Industries stock, which currently sold at thirty-five and a quarter dollars per share.

As rumors of a takeover circulated, the price of EBE stock had risen and was now twenty-one dollars, two dollars, or points, higher than on Tuesday. Although further increases could be expected, most of the people Caroline had spoken with favored an acquisition by Olympia Industries. Caroline felt that they would vote for Lyle's slate of directors, should he propose one, simply because their shares of Olympia Industries would be worth so much more than their shares of EBE.

Caroline confidently pointed out that EBE was in a strong position in competing for several major military contracts this year and that she expected both stock prices and dividends to rise. The shareholders were interested in what she had to say, but wanted performance rather than promises.

Now she told Sam Hanover, "We'd better prepare something for the mail." Her very real concern was hidden by a businesslike tone. "Will you work out some figures on anticipated sales, profits, and dividends and get them to me? I'll draft a letter to the shareholders. We have to convince them that over the long term they'll be better off if EBE stays independent."

For just a moment Caroline read uncertainty—even worry—in Sam's eyes. The peculiar expression disappeared so rapidly that she had to wonder if she was being imaginative. Just to make certain, she brought up the subject of the weapons contracts on which EBE had bid.

"It would be accurate to say that our financial picture is extremely positive, wouldn't it, Sam? We *are* favored on at least two of those contracts?"

"You know we are, Carrie." Sam was once again poker-faced, his bland accountant's demeanor reassuringly in place. "Especially on the radar-jamming system—it's included in the design of the company producing the missile, and rumor has it that our design is a big factor in why they have the inside track on the contract. I'll get those numbers to you early next week." He stood up, started toward the door, and then stopped. "By the way, are you going to call a special meeting of the board of directors?" he asked, looking back over his shoulder.

Caroline permitted herself a tired sigh. "Yes, we'll have to do that. Next Friday at ten?"

"Can you have the letter drafted by then?"

"Yes. I'll ask Maggie to make the calls." Caroline followed him into the outer office, where Maggie sat working on the company's annual report.

Caroline had inherited Maggie O'Connell from her late husband, who had hired her fresh out of business school over ten years before. She considered Maggie one of her strongest assets. Maggie was more administrative assistant than secretary now—an intelligent, competent woman who knew as much about EBE as anyone, with the possible exceptions of Caroline and Sam. Her petite stature, breathless voice, and long, unruly red curls had coaxed confidences from more than one disarmed executive, but most of all Caroline prized Maggie for her warmth and humor.

Maggie was the closest friend she had, either in business or out of it. Caroline tended to make people uncomfortable, mostly because she refused to discuss any aspect of her personal life, while others were only too free with their confidences. They could never know of her compelling need to put the last few traumatic years behind her. Yet in spite of all she had suffered, she still felt a strong loyalty to her late husband. If she were to speak of just how tormented her years with him had been, people would remember only that Clay Spencer had turned cruel and obsessive and forget that for fifty-five years of his life he had been a gentle, caring human being.

Maggie, however, had been Clay's private secretary. She had spent as many hours with him each week as Caroline and was thus the only person in the world who really understood just what his wife had been through. Their shared tribulations had resulted in a warm, if usually unspoken, empathy.

Caroline briefly summarized her last two conversations with Sam Hanover, then asked Maggie to call the other five members of the board of directors. Only Sam and herself were "inside" members: Executives of the firm. The others were prominent businessmen or civic leaders.

To the outside world Caroline McKay Spencer would never admit that the takeover attempt had caught her off guard or that she was at all concerned about losing control of the company. Even with Sam Hanover she was careful to sound businesslike and confident. But Maggie was the one person she trusted wholeheartedly, and as they spoke Caroline leaned wearily against her desk, a worried frown on her face. She was not particularly surprised that Maggie appeared to have little reaction to the news. Obviously she was already aware of Lyle's maneuvers—she seemed to have a pipeline to all the best gossips in Seattle.

"I don't like the odds." Caroline sighed. "Matthew Lyle's track record is just too darn good. I checked our files on him yesterday, Maggie. Do you know that in the last ten years only one company's gotten away from him? They merged with a third corporation rather than let Lyle get control, but I don't want to do that."

Maggie O'Connell's lips curved upward into a smile that brought a sparkle to her green eyes. "Well, then," she said with the lilting Irish brogue she liked to affect whenever the atmosphere became too tense, "he'll just be findin' out that Elliot Bay is going to be the second—won't he now?"

Caroline laughed, her good humor restored, and went back to work.

By the following Friday, as she sat at the head of the rectangular conference table in the company's redwood-paneled boardroom, she was forced to acknowledge both to herself and to the board that EBE's future as an independent corporation was indeed precarious. During the past week several items had appeared in the business sections of the local papers questioning whether or not Matthew Lyle intended to take over EBE. The man certainly wasn't reticent about giving interviews, Caroline thought acidly, although he had yet to commit himself to any course of action. As for herself, she met reporters' questions with an enchanting smile and a polite, "No comment." She explained that she would make a statement after she had discussed the situation with her board.

The meeting lasted through lunch. After a thorough

discussion of the company's options, it was obvious that only Caroline and Sam really favored a refusal to negotiate with Matthew Lyle. Such a stand would probably mean digging in the corporate heels for an expensive, difficult proxy fight.

In order to solicit proxies—the right to vote for absent shareholders at the annual meeting—Matthew Lyle would first have to register his intention with the federal Securities and Exchange Commission. Thus far he had not done so; perhaps he was hoping to avoid such a step. Most of the board members, feeling it unwise to get involved in a fight they might well lose, were anxious to find some middle ground between cooperating with a takeover bid and bitterly opposing one.

Matthew Lyle, they suggested, might be willing to sell his shares back to the company at a handsome profit. Or perhaps he would accept a seat on the board of directors, satisfied that this would give him a voice in company policy. Either action required the approval of the shareholders.

Two members—one a banker, the other the president of a local company—urged the board to agree to a friendly acquisition, whereby Elliot Bay Electronics would become a division of Olympia Industries. Caroline winced inwardly. Obviously Lyle had brought them—and their four percent of the stock—around to his point of view. She could accept the wisdom of negotiating, but vehemently opposed a sellout. She had studied Lyle's past takeovers, and while he generally avoided savaging the entire management of a company he acquired, he invariably made significant changes. Caroline had little doubt that she would be among those receiving a pink slip, since Lyle usually brought in his own president in cases of forced acquisition. But she had no intention of submissively offering her neck to the ax Matthew Lyle would wield.

Ultimately, the board compromised. With minor changes, the letter that Caroline had drafted would be sent to the shareholders, urging them to retain the present board. Caroline reluctantly agreed to request a meeting with Matthew Lyle, preferably to arrange to buy him out or, as a more distasteful alternative, to offer him not more than two seats on the board of directors.

Caroline's letter was printed up and mailed out the following Monday, and within days the company had a positive response to it. Several major shareholders called Caroline personally, telling her that they were willing to wait until the company's annual meeting in May before making a decision on any slate of board members that Matthew Lyle might propose.

Setting up a meeting with the arrogant Seattle entrepreneur proved to be a more difficult endeavor. "He has all the time in the world for *reporters*," Caroline told Maggie on Wednesday afternoon, fuming. "Why is he avoiding *me?*"

Maggie shook her head. "I just don't know, Caroline. I called his office on Monday to set up an appointment and his secretary said she would get back to me. When she called this morning she sounded genuinely apologetic. She said, and I quote, 'I'm sorry, but Mr. Lyle will be unavailable for the next several weeks.' I asked her if he would be in town and she admitted that he only has one trip scheduled during the next two weeks. I just don't know what to make of it."

"If it weren't so undignified, I'd march myself over to that fancy new Fourth Avenue office of his and demand to know why he's playing games with me," Caroline snapped out, her fit of temper causing Maggie to grin with amusement.

"Now that would be a sight to see!" Maggie teased in her mock Irish drawl. Her eyes traveled dramatically up and down Caroline's figure, businesslike yet sensual in a plaid wool skirt and nubby hand-knit sweater. "The ever-so-cool Caroline McKay Spencer losing her temper in public. Of course," she went on, with a calculating gleam in her green eyes, "Matthew Lyle hardly hides himself in a cave, Caroline. You could arrange, an—uh—*accidental* meeting."

"No doubt," was the acid reply. "All I'd have to do is walk into one of the local newspapers! But what would I have to gain by it?"

"He's human, isn't he? And *very* male? And obviously not blind, given the gorgeous women he's always photographed with," Maggie pointed out.

Caroline was well aware that others considered her beautiful, but she remembered her days as an awkward schoolgirl and could never quite believe they were right. She had a flawless fair complexion, light blue eyes tinged with green, and a facial structure that was delicately exotic, like a model's. Her nose was small and straight, her mouth delightfully curved, and with the addition of the long blonde hair she wore parted in the center and pinned back from her oval face in a neat bun, the overall impression was one of cool, intimidating perfection. Her expensive designer clothing hung gracefully on her long-legged, lithe frame.

Apparently a certain breed of man took this sculptured beauty and her reserved personality as a challenge. These aggressive males were not content to wait until a respectable period of mourning had elapsed after Clay's death, but had begun to pursue her a scant month after the funeral. They implied that since Clay Spencer had been extremely ill for almost a year before his death, his widow must be pining for their virile company. She made it quite clear that she was pining for no such thing.

As the president of a successful local corporation, Caroline accepted certain obligations, but always chose a safe older man, like the widowed Sam Hanover, as her escort. These men understood their role and kept their distance. Caroline had no intention of losing either her heart or her independence to any overbearing man with an overinflated opinion of himself.

She understood the implication of Maggie's remark, but used humor to dismiss it. "Matthew Lyle, smitten with lust into abandoning his dastardly takeover scheme?" she asked, an eyebrow cocked dubiously. She shook her head. "I doubt it, Maggie. He's a hard-nosed businessman, not an impressionable kid."

"I've seen the way men look at you," Maggie persisted. "Matthew Lyle doesn't need EBE, and the fact is, he hasn't filed anything with the S.E.C. yet. For some reason he still hasn't really made up his mind whether to go after us, and it wouldn't hurt to flash him one of your devastating smiles and soften him up a little. He won't be immune to your charms."

"I'd rather charm a snake!"

Maggie sighed in exasperation. "Listen to me, Caroline Spencer. The boat show opens this Friday. There's a long article in today's paper about it. It says that Lyle Marine Construction will be getting an award from one of the big magazines in the yachting field—a special prize for one of its models. From what I've heard, Lyle Marine is very dear to the elusive Matthew's heart. Ten to one he shows up to collect his trophy in person."

"Honestly, Maggie, what am I supposed to do? Hide

behind a camper and waylay him in the Kingdome parking lot when he comes out?" Caroline had begun to giggle, her laughter as enchanting as it was uncharacteristic. "You're wasting your time as my executive assistant. You should write movie scripts!"

"All the same, Caroline, I'm going to call Lyle Marine and see when they're scheduled to get that award. I'll find out who's accepting it, too. And if it's the big enchilada himself, whether you go or not is up to you!"

"I'll send you instead," Caroline teased. "Matthew Lyle might like fiery Irish redheads."

"I don't think Jerry would let me do it." Maggie smiled back and gathered up her papers, leaving Caroline's office.

Caroline shook her head and reached for a manila folder containing some correspondence that Maggie had brought in for her signature. She thought privately that if Jerry Carlisle was so possessive of Maggie he should somehow persuade her to marry him instead of contenting himself with simply living with her. Maggie had divorced her first husband several years before, after a brief, unhappy marriage, and was leery about taking a second stab at wedded bliss.

In any event Caroline didn't presume to make judgments on anyone else's personal life. She knew that Maggie had begun to date Jerry only after her divorce and was anything but promiscuous. But many of Caroline's schoolmates had jumped from bed to bed with baffling abandon during college, and she simply couldn't understand why they bothered. Such behavior didn't seem to make them happy—except for a few minutes or hours in the arms of their lovers. Perhaps she was puzzled because of her own lack of experience in such matters; if the man existed who could raise her pulse rate even one iota, she had yet to meet him. No tongues of flame had ever scorched her skin, and at times she had wondered if there was something physically wrong with her.

At the moment, however, she was much too busy to worry about her social life. She had work to do.

—

Chapter Two

The following Monday Maggie strolled into Caroline's office with a smug smile securely plastered on her face. "Guess who I've been talking to?" she drawled, then went on with scarcely a pause. "The public relations department over at Olympia Industries, that's who. Lyle Marine Construction is getting that award tomorrow afternoon at two, Mrs. Spencer, and our favorite corporate pirate is dropping by to collect it in person."

Caroline stared for several seconds at the report on her desk, then lifted frigid blue eyes and fixed them on her secretary. "I have work to do, Maggie. Was there anything *important* you wanted to tell me?"

But after all those years of putting up with Clay Spencer, Maggie O'Connell had developed a tough hide and a discerning ear. "You don't fool me," she said. "You're sorely tempted, Caroline Spencer." Then she laughed and sauntered out the door.

Caroline swiveled her chair toward the window and

stared out at King County Stadium—the Kingdome—
only blocks away from her building. For many years the
administrative offices of EBE had been located at the
company's original plant in the most industrialized area
of West Seattle. But with lucrative defense contracts
filling EBE's coffers, Clay Spencer had decided that
office space in downtown Seattle better befitted his
thriving corporation. The original plant in West Seattle
continued to be the site of nonmilitary manufacturing;
weapons systems were built at their new factory in
Renton, south of Seattle.

She turned back to her desk, impatient with her own
thoughts. Yet during the rest of Monday and all
through Tuesday morning, she had difficulty in concen-
trating on the columns of numbers in front of her. Her
attention persisted in wandering to Matthew Lyle.
What was behind the man's arrogant refusal to grant
her a few moments of his precious time? Was he playing
hard to get? Did he get a kick out of making all of them
squirm?

She had no intention of even speaking to the man
when she buzzed Maggie and asked her to call a cab.
Lyle was too hard-bitten to be swayed by feminine
beauty or charm. She only knew that she had been
seized by a compelling urge to view him in the flesh.
She ignored Maggie's teasing laughter. After all, she
told herself, scouting the enemy was only sensible
strategy. Lyle would never even know she had come.

It was drizzling lightly when Caroline pushed open
the heavy glass door of her building. She pulled up the
hood of her all-weather coat as she dashed to the
waiting taxicab. Dismal weather never depressed her;
anyone who grew up in the Pacific Northwest learned to
smile indulgently at overcast skies and rain. Liquid
sunshine, the natives called it. But when the clouds

cleared to reveal the genuine article, there was no place on earth more beautiful than Washington. Caroline wouldn't have traded the sights and smells of her native forests, waters, and mountains for any amount of boring Sun Belt sunshine.

The Kingdome, with its huge steel and concrete roof and climate-controlled interior, sat on a thirty-six-acre site not far from the original Seattle settlement of 1852. It housed professional and college sports, trade shows, and a wide variety of special events. Today, Caroline was greeted by a mass of color as hundreds of sail and power boats stood lined up on the stadium floor. She walked up and down the red-carpeted aisles until she came to the Lyle Marine exhibit. The company's forty-foot racing yacht, the LM 40, was prominently displayed: the crown jewel of a royal line.

She picked up a brochure; it boasted of the yacht's winning performances in race after race, often in competition against even more expensive, customized craft. A glance over the technical description of the yacht's merits meant nothing to her. Although sailing was a hobby with many Seattle residents and a virtual obsession with others, neither her father nor her late husband had owned a boat. Alex McKay had once remarked that he was quite content to make money from the people who did.

It was just after one thirty; Caroline occupied the half hour until the awards ceremony by strolling around the stadium, looking over the models on display. She peeked inside several boats, admiring compact, luxurious cabins that made her wish she were a better sailor. She had a distressing tendency to become motion sick in anything smaller than a Washington State Ferry. There was something deeply appealing about cruising through Puget Sound, perhaps as far as Vancouver,

British Columbia, in one of these sleek, expensive boats. She craved the solitude, the independence.

After a few minutes she removed her coat and slung it over her arm, revealing a dove-gray blouson tunic dress with long sleeves and a turtleneck. The knit fabric caressed her body, accentuating her height and her slender curves. Caroline had never been self-conscious about her five feet eight-and-a-half-inch frame, and in her medium-heeled boots she was taller than many of the men she passed.

By the time she returned to the Lyle Marine exhibit, a sizable audience had gathered around the LM 40. Several photographers clicked away as two men emerged from the yacht and stood on deck. Both smiled. The taller man's eyes flickered over the crowd, apparently missing the willowy platinum blonde on its fringes. The shorter man appeared to be the publisher of *Racing Yachtsman* magazine. Someone handed him a microphone, whereupon he launched into an effusive and lengthy paean to the LM 40. Electronic flashes blinked as he handed the plaque to Matthew Lyle. Lyle accepted with a handshake and took the mike.

"Thank you, Roger," he drawled. "I couldn't have said it better myself. All of us at LMC are pleased and honored." They repeated the handshake, obediently posing for the photographers.

Caroline stared up at him, thinking that those cold newspaper photographs of him didn't begin to do him justice! Even his well-tailored three-piece suit couldn't hide the leashed dynamism of the man. She could picture him on the deck of his boat during a race, the wind whipping through his longish dark hair, the yacht tossed about by high waves, his lean, powerful body braced for action, controlling the rolling craft. If ever a man could be characterized as ruggedly handsome, it was Matthew Lyle. There was nothing gentle about his dark, heavy brows or firm jaw, and not even the little cleft in his chin could detract from the toughness of his looks.

No wonder women fell all over him! Other women, she mentally corrected—not Caroline McKay Spencer. If she were studying him, it was merely to size him up. Ultimately, she turned away, embarrassed about the length of time she had spent staring. He was only a man, and a merciless, ruthless one at that.

She walked back to her office, ostensibly because the rain had stopped. In fact, she wanted to sort out her emotions. Matthew Lyle disturbed her. His sheer physical presence was intimidating, she acknowledged, as was his business reputation. Could she really handle him?

By the time Caroline reached her office, she was merely annoyed by her own lack of confidence. Of course she could handle him. When Maggie greeted her with a sly look and demanded to know what had happened, she replied airily, "I didn't speak to him. I just watched. He's very handsome and charming and he probably thinks he's every woman's dream. But if he thinks he's going to use that sex appeal of his on *me*, he's got the wrong lady!"

"No doubt," Maggie agreed, eyes twinkling.

Caroline ignored her secretary's subtle teasing and settled herself back at her desk. She had a number of real problems to deal with, chief among them a serious supply delay. She knew that it behooved her to turn her attention to cajoling rare metals out of reluctant dealers rather than waste her time on thoughts of Matthew Lyle.

She let another week go by before asking Maggie to ring his office once again. By then she was able to explain her earlier diffidence by telling herself she had simply believed too many of Lyle's press releases. When they actually met, she would react with her usual confidence and aplomb. But that meeting would not be in the next few weeks. Lyle's secretary had repeated that he had "no time available in which to see Mrs. Spencer." Or, as Maggie fliply put it, "Don't call us, we'll call you."

Caroline had merely laughed, too busy to sit and brood about the man's refusal to see her. In addition to her usual responsibilities she was busy with preparations for the annual shareholders' meeting in May. She was determined to march into that meeting and deliver the most glowing report to stockholders in the firm's history. But she knew that wouldn't happen unless everyone in the company worked overtime to *make* it happen, and as far as she was concerned, the meeting with Lyle could wait.

Elliot Bay Electronics was scheduled to exhibit its navigational systems at an industrial trade show during the final week of February. Since electronic components took up much less space than yachts, the show was being held not in the huge Kingdome, but rather in the Exhibition Hall at Seattle Center, the cultural and civic complex that now occupied the grounds of the 1962 World's Fair. Caroline had personally supervised the design and production of the company's exhibit and was eager to see how well the display would succeed as a showcase for EBE's products.

She slipped out of the office late Thursday morning and hopped a fare-free bus down to the Alweg Monorail, another artifact of the 1962 fair. Once there had been talk of extending the system down to the Seattle–Tacoma International Airport—or Sea–Tac Airport, as it was called—but currently it ran only from downtown Seattle to Seattle Center, making the 1.2 mile trip in ninety seconds.

The city was bathed in welcome sunshine, the azure sky dotted with occasional puffy cumulus clouds. Caroline had left her overcoat at the office. She wore a steel-blue, wool-blend suit; the skirt was straight with a side slit, and the fitted waist-length jacket had frog closings. The turtleneck of her gray cashmere sweater peeked up above the collar of the jacket, helping to keep her warm on this crisp, late-winter day.

The weather was so dazzling that Caroline succumbed to a sudden longing to ride to the observation deck of the Space Needle, the 600-foot steel tower that had been a symbol of Seattle ever since the World's Fair. She hadn't been up there since her college days, and she fell in love with her home state all over again as she gazed through the windows at the spectacular vistas that surrounded the city. The snow-capped peaks of the Cascade Mountains on one side and the Olympic Mountains on the other rose out of a light haze; in the foreground were the waters of Lake Washington to the east and Elliot Bay and Puget Sound to the west. Blown-up photographs above each window were labeled with the names of buildings and geographical features, enabling the viewer to identify what he saw. Caroline noticed that it was time to replace some of them; new buildings, constructed during the last few years, were absent from the current pictures.

After descending the Space Needle, she went into the Food Circus for something to eat. The area featured an array of self-service stands offering diverse ethnic concoctions. After a few moments Caroline decided on a slice of unexotic cheese pizza and a large soft drink, which she carried outside with her. Music from the

International Fountain caught her ear and she wandered over to listen, watching the constantly changing patterns of water as she juggled her food. It really was a glorious day, she thought, totally mesmerized by the way the sunshine played over the columns of spray. Finally, with a reluctant sigh, she started to turn away, intending to go over to the Exhibit Hall.

She realized that someone was behind her only as she crashed into a human wall, the cola in her paper cup sloshing out onto the man's suit. "Oh!" she exclaimed. "I'm terribly sorry." Then she looked up into the man's eyes.

Caroline never lost her composure in public, but now she felt her face go pale. She had just spilled sticky brown soda all over the jacket of Matthew Lyle's expensive tan suit. He reached into his pocket and produced a pristine white handkerchief, with which he dabbed at the dripping garment. Then he smiled down at her. "No harm done. It's not every day that someone so beautiful stains my clothing."

To her utter amazement, Caroline found herself blushing, something she hadn't done since she was a teenager. If Matthew Lyle was handsome when seen from a distance, up this close he was positively overwhelming. There was no point denying the effect he had on her. Just his smile made her tingle all over.

But her instinctive defense system soon clicked into place, and she appeared totally composed as she said, in a cool tone wholly at odds with the warmth spreading through her, "Please send me the bill. I should have looked where I was going."

His amused smile confused her. Six-foot, four-inch specimens of rugged masculinity did not usually stare down at her with such indulgence, and she was at a complete loss as to how to proceed. Should she introduce herself and raise the subject of his intentions toward EBE? Or should she simply hand him a business card with her address on it and haughtily excuse herself?

While she was debating the issue, he drawled, "I can afford to pay for my own dry cleaning bill." Then he added, "But you *do* owe me something for the inconvenience, and I expect to collect, Miss . . . ?"

He cocked one of those dark brows expectantly, and Caroline was aware of the most overwhelming compulsion not to tell him who she really was. He gave no sign of recognizing her. Her left hand was bare of a gold band. She had discarded the ring two months after Clay's death because it was too painful a reminder of her marriage.

"McKay," she found herself saying. "Carrie McKay." She forced herself to breathe evenly, disguising her anxiety as to whether he would connect her name with Elliot Bay Electronics.

No glimmer of recognition lit up his deep brown eyes. He simply smiled and once again asserted, "I won't let you go until we settle the question of repayment, Carrie. Come to dinner and the opera with me this Saturday night and I'll forgive you for the stain on my suit."

Caroline was appalled at how badly she wanted to say yes. Her reaction had nothing to do with Maggie's Machiavellian scheme to charm the man into submission and everything to do with the fact that *he* was charming *her* into the same languid state. She told herself firmly, however, that as far as Matthew Lyle was concerned they were total strangers.

"I'm sorry," she said in a dismissively cool tone of voice. "We don't even know each other." She took two steps toward the Exhibition Hall, only to feel his fingers clamp themselves around her upper arms, pull her firmly but gently backward, and turn her around.

"My name is Matthew Lyle. I assure you that I'm reasonably respectable." Caroline, her heart thudding from his touch, managed to gaze back blandly, as though the name meant absolutely nothing to her. "I'm the chairman of Olympia Industries, here in Seattle," he added, releasing her. He seemed to be amused by something. Her ignorance? Or her resistance?

A little demon prodded Caroline to tease this self-assured creature, and she didn't bother resisting it. "Oh!" she said brightly. "I saw your picture in the paper. You're the one who built that prizewinning boat!" Then she went on suspiciously, "Are you married?"

He laughed, a deep, resonant sound that Caroline found far too captivating. When he smiled or laughed, there was no trace of the ruthless business executive. He looked irresistibly boyish, in spite of the gray strands of hair at his temples. "No, I'm not married," he replied, "but if I were, you would tempt me to forget she even existed."

Caroline felt her face heat up all over again. Why couldn't she come up with a suitably witty response instead of standing here like a tongue-tied adolescent?

"Would you like to see my driver's license and two major credit cards?" he went on, tongue firmly in cheek.

Caroline located her scattered wits. "That won't be necessary, Mr. Lyle. I'm not loaning you money or cashing a check for you. I'm not even going out with you," she parried.

He ignored her refusal. "Tell me where you live. I'll pick you up at five thirty."

When she shook her head, Matthew Lyle's hand shot

out to her shoulder, sliding her purse into his possession and sending ripples of heat through her in the process. He tugged at the closed zipper, presumably intent on checking her driver's license to discover her address. All of Caroline's identification was in her married name, and she didn't want him to find out who she was—at least, not yet. She hastily grabbed the purse back from him.

"You don't give up, do you?"

"Saturday at five thirty, Carrie. What's your address?"

With feigned reluctance, Caroline told him that she lived on Mercer Island and supplied the street number. "The house backs onto the lake," she volunteered. "The drive is very steep. I'll meet you at the top of the hill."

"All right. I'll look forward to it, Carrie." He bent down, brushed his mouth over hers, and added softly, "Don't keep me waiting." Then he disappeared into the crowd of lunching office workers and students.

Caroline's emotions were wholly dazed as she walked to the industrial trade show. She had never met anyone like Matthew Lyle. If any other man had tossed out that outrageous line about forgetting his wife's existence, she would have laughed in his face. But Lyle had a way of looking at a woman, his lips curved into a crooked half-smile, his eyes seeing nothing but her face, that breathed seductively, "You've bewitched me. I can't wait to make love to you." Caroline cursed herself for a susceptible idiot—he probably used that same intense gaze on all his women. But she knew she would be waiting for him when he drove up on Saturday.

As she inspected the EBE exhibit, she had trouble thinking of anything but Matthew Lyle. Not that the display wasn't first-rate—it was, easily one of the best in the show. But as she strolled around the Exhibition Hall, she found herself musing that it had been an incredible coincidence to literally bump into Lyle here at Seattle Center. Why wasn't he at his office? Had he taken a few hours off to inspect the electronic equipment at this very show? Olympia Industries probably dealt with several of the exhibiting companies. Or had he been seduced by the beauty of the day into playing hookey for a little while and found himself drawn to the spraying waters of the fountain? Caroline preferred the latter, fanciful explanation.

Friday dragged by, with thoughts of Matthew Lyle constantly intruding to disturb Caroline's peace of mind. Over the years she had learned to avoid emotional attachments of any sort. When you cared about someone, you gave that person power to hurt you.

Her mother, Ingrid, whom she remembered only vaguely as a sweet if ineffectual woman, had died when Caroline was only six. Two years later, Alex McKay had purchased part of Adam Spencer's stock in EBE, becoming Clay's new business partner in the process.

Caroline supposed that her father had been a classic workaholic. He had channeled all his effort and energy into the business. He had no time for his gangly daughter, whom he left to a succession of disapproving housekeepers. Over the years Clay Spencer had been far kinder to her than Alex McKay had. Clay had been a bewildering figure to a child—brilliant yet oddly simple, gentle yet remote. She decided that a part of his mind never left the laboratory.

Caroline had always found it ironic that for all Alex's compulsive work, social and financial success eluded him. Perhaps the former meant nothing to him, but money would have been a symbol of his importance in the world. She suspected that her father would have preferred his home to be more elegant than their modest two-bedroom ranch located in a middle-class suburb of Seattle. As Caroline grew up, he might even have dressed her in something other than ordinary chain-store clothing, just to show off his wealth.

But then, designer labels would have been wasted on her in those days. Every year she sprouted still taller than her classmates, a string bean of a tomboy who trailed around after the neighborhood boys and learned to play basketball on a five-man boys' team before anyone told her that the girls' version of the game took six.

A few of Alex's housekeepers tried to get her out of scruffy jeans and into tailored skirts, regarding her occasional cuts and bruises with unsympathetic frowns. Caroline ignored them. She played basketball as well as any of the boys, and if torn jeans and scraped knees were the price of acceptance and companionship, she gladly paid it.

Caroline's father died of a heart attack when she was sixteen. She cried only once, at the funeral, and felt guilty at her inability to truly mourn him. Her only other family were cousins of her mother's who lived on the East Coast. In truth, Caroline was more distressed over her uncertain future than over the death of a man who had barely acknowledged her existence.

When Clay Spencer had invited her to make her home with him, she was both relieved and pleased. Clay was both kind and easygoing, wrapped up in his research but far less compulsive than her father had been. She quickly accepted his offer.

The next two years were the happiest of her life. Clay worked on and perfected a new electronic surveillance and jamming system. In order to finance a new factory to build the machine, EBE became a public corporation, with both Caroline and Clay releasing part of their holdings for sale to the general public as stock.

Caroline had little interest in the money she acquired as a result and no great enthusiasm for the stunning contemporary home that Clay purchased on exclusive Mercer Island in Lake Washington, east of Seattle. She was happy because Clay was happy, uncharacteristically pleased by his sudden financial success.

Unlike her father, Clay was genuinely fond of her; he treated her as a cherished daughter and often spoke of his concern and affection for her. Even though he spent as much time in his laboratory as Alex had in the office, when he was home he gave Caroline his full attention. She easily filled her free hours. She was firmly entrenched as "one of the guys" now, her tall, ungainly figure acquiring unexpected grace the minute her sneakered feet made contact with a basketball court.

Then, during her last year in high school, Caroline's body began to mature until she was a stunningly willowy creature, as poised and graceful in her Italian leather pumps as she had ever been in basketball sneakers. Her schoolmates appeared to disregard the enticements of her slender, high-breasted figure and platinum-blonde hair and continued to treat her as they always had, but the rest of the world was not so oblivious. By the middle of the summer, gossip as to her position in Clay Spencer's house was circulating so freely that even Caroline was aware of it.

She thought it absurd. Clay was a handsome, virile man, and he enjoyed the company of women, but he looked every one of his fifty-five years. The idea of a romance between them was preposterous. Nonetheless, Caroline was over eighteen now, and she told Clay she felt it would be best if she moved into her own apartment. To her amazement, he countered with a proposal of marriage.

Even though his offer was couched in language that indicated he was primarily concerned about her future, Caroline had no doubt that he meant to be her husband in every sense of the word. She never hesitated in turning him down. She was tremendously flattered and readily admitted her deep affection for him. He had been exceptionally kind to her, especially during the past two years. But she thought of him as a father rather than a lover and, like most girls her age, dreamed of passionate moonlit encounters with handsome, dynamic men. Clay tried to change her mind by insisting that she was too naive to be left on her own, but Caroline refused to be swayed. She began looking for an apartment close to the University of Washington in Seattle, which she would be attending that fall.

Over the next four and a half years, she tried not to ask herself what might have happened if Clay had not become so dreadfully sick. Even at their most optimistic, his doctors gave him only eighteen months to live. When Clay took her hand, told her he needed her, and pleaded with her to marry him, Caroline was forced to reconsider her rejection of his proposal.

His surgery had left him incapable of becoming a normal husband to her, although that fact was known only to Clay, Caroline, and the doctors. Clay made it clear that he expected no more than companionship from her. One of his arguments was that he wanted to make certain that Elliot Bay Electronics remained "in the family," as he put it, and Caroline did not pretend to misunderstand which part of the family he meant. He and Adam had barely spoken since their father's death, and Clay seemed haunted by the idea that somehow his brother would eventually wrest control of the company away from Caroline. He was afraid that if he simply left his shares in EBE to Caroline without marrying her, Adam, as his sole surviving relative, would successfully challenge the will. As Clay's widow, however, there would be no question that Caroline would legally inherit both the stock and control of the company.

Caroline was not attracted to Clay's money. She was swayed only by how desperately frightened he seemed to be, by how much he appeared to need her. He had given her the only real happiness she could remember, and a year or eighteen months of devotion was almost too little to offer in return. She gladly became his wife and forced herself to shrug off the sarcastic comments about the difference in their ages and the malicious assumption on the part of almost everyone that she had married him with the sole motive of eventually inheriting his money. No one suspected how serious his illness was—he kept quiet for business reasons—and Caroline did not want to think about the inevitable scathing gossip that would surface when he died.

With Clay's approval and encouragement, she entered college as scheduled. They went on as before, but now their roles were reversed, with Caroline providing affection, support, and almost maternal comforting. At first, Clay's illness did not prevent him from continuing with his research, but he lacked the energy to continue as chief administrator as well. Sam Hanover took over the day-to-day details of running the company, although he retained the formal title of controller.

In high school Caroline had thought about combining her love of both sports and children by preparing herself for a career in teaching physical education. But Clay had other plans for her. He wanted her to major in business administration, and even though she had no particular interest in the subject, she agreed. It seemed to make him happy, and besides, it was not forever—only for a year or two.

Two years stretched into three and then four. For the first few years the change in Clay was gradual, so that Caroline scarcely noticed herself adapting to it. She accepted the fact that he was often demanding and petulant. The longer he lived, the more obsessed he became—both with Caroline and with his business. At times he was exhausted from his illness and physically sick from the powerful medications he took, but he drove himself relentlessly, and drove Caroline as well.

He had decided that she must prepare herself to assume the presidency of Elliot Bay Electronics when he died. Not only did he expect her to earn top grades; he insisted that she spend every spare moment of her time working with him or Sam, learning the business. Fortunately, Caroline learned to enjoy certain aspects of business administration, but even had she hated every bit of it, she would not have rebelled against the verbal whip Clay so often flailed her with. She reminded herself that he had been very good to her, both when she was a child and after her father's death. He was a sick man who could die at any time and was not really responsible for his actions. It was her duty to take care of him.

In the year before his death life with Clay became almost intolerable for Caroline. She knew that if she let herself feel the pain he unwittingly inflicted the trauma would destroy her. Her only recourse was to retreat behind a stoic facade, pretend to be amenable and understanding, and refuse to let herself resent her lack of independence. Her only outlet was sports, and if as a freshman her male classmates had almost laughed her out of the gym when she asked to join in their casual games of basketball, a demonstration of her quick, agile play soon won her a regular spot on one of the teams.

At five feet, eight and a half inches, Caroline was shorter than most of the men, but made up for her handicap with quick footwork and accurate shooting. She pretended not to notice the admiring stares at the way she filled out her T-shirt and shorts. Propositions were met with a friendly reminder of her married status. She was aware that her opponents were sometimes less rough with her than with her teammates and felt rather grateful for it. She was seldom fouled, and when it happened too often, her protective teammates were quick to chew out the offending party.

On a basketball court she could forget about Caroline Spencer and revert to being Carrie McKay. Although Clay disapproved of her participation in these games, Caroline refused to give them up. She steadfastly ignored his tirades about sports being unfeminine and unsuitable for a married woman. Physical exercise acted as a tonic which she desperately needed, and at times she felt that only the companionship and acceptance of the boys she played with allowed her to bear life with Clay. Even after her graduation and his death she had continued her participation in the sport because she loved the game and because it gave her a way to work out the emotions she refused to let herself express.

After graduating from college, Caroline joined the company's marketing department, selling nonmilitary equipment to small companies in both North America and Europe. Clay Spencer was hospitalized the following October after a difficult three months at home. Caroline felt obligated to stop working in order to take care of him full time, but Clay insisted that she hire a nurse and continue learning the business.

When she was at home, however, she coped with his fits of temper and unjustified criticism by retreating even further behind her defensive screen. She blocked out what she did not wish to hear.

Clay spent the last month of his life in a coma. By the time he died Caroline could not pretend to feel any particular grief. Her mourning had been gradual, extending back through the four and a half years when she had watched the kind, unworldly man she married die, to be replaced by a cold, driven, unfeeling creature who bore no resemblance to the real Clay Spencer. With a twinge of guilt, she silently acknowledged a sense of release at his death. Never again, she promised herself, would she give another human being the power to dominate her as Clay had done. She had learned to value her independence and would never again risk losing it.

The board of directors of Elliot Bay Electronics Corporation met four days after the funeral. At the urging of Sam Hanover, they proposed that Caroline, as Clay's widow and Alex's daughter, should assume the leadership of the company.

Caroline was intelligent enough to understand both her strengths and weaknesses. Her own vulnerability led her to erect barriers in her personal relationships, and she was cool and aloof with all the men she met socially. Business was a separate matter. She could be charming and persuasive with EBE's customers and was well liked by them. Because of who she was, the firm's employees would accept her selection as president, as would the stockholders. She had both a talent for administration and a satisfactory understanding of the technical aspects of the business.

On the other hand, corporate finance bored her. Talk of return on equity, after-tax margins, and earnings per share tended to leave her eyes glazed. Now she would have to take the responsibility for EBE's performance. Fortunately, she could rely on Sam Hanover to teach her what she needed to know.

Once assured of the board's support, Caroline was no longer troubled by doubts. To the amazement of all six men in the room, she made it clear that she was no fool. She knew quite well that her selection was largely a symbolic act meant to reassure long-standing nonmilitary customers that EBE was still a family venture committed to personalized service. But she did not intend to be anyone's puppet.

True to her word, she immediately moved to consolidate her position. Driven by memories of servitude under the boot of Clay Spencer, she swore to herself that she, Caroline McKay Spencer, was going to be in charge. During the past thirteen months she had worked herself harder than Clay ever had and was just beginning to feel in real command of the business. If there was a part of her that longed to abandon responsibilities that were unusually heavy for someone only twenty-four years old, she resolutely forced it down, along with most of her other emotions.

She was friendly but formal in the office. Only Sam Hanover ever addressed her by her childhood nickname of Carrie, while a handful of others, such as Maggie O'Connell, called her Caroline. To everyone else, she was Mrs. Spencer.

Maggie had once told her that most of her rejected

male suitors referred to her by a different name: Mount Carrie. The nickname was taken from a lofty, 7,000-foot ice-capped peak in the Olympic Mountain range west of Seattle, and Caroline supposed it fit. She could hardly argue with a name that alluded to her height, and no one would ever find out that her cool, distant facade hid a very vulnerable nature.

Chapter Three

For a few minutes on Thursday, during her conversation with Matthew Lyle, Caroline knew that she had almost become the Carrie McKay of five years ago. She had found herself living a fantasy—that of being swept off her feet by a magnetically handsome, twentieth-century merchant prince. Caroline Spencer was far too wary to let any man penetrate her defenses, but yesterday, for just a little while, the bruising years with Clay might never have existed.

She realized that her primary motivation for deceiving Matthew Lyle about her identity had nothing to do with business, but rather stemmed from the fact that, as Caroline McKay Spencer she automatically reacted in a cool and sophisticated manner. She had created that image for herself because it was safe, never expecting that it might trap her.

But when she was near Matthew Lyle, she felt

anything but cool and sophisticated. She didn't want a business dispute to interfere in their relationship. Of course, there was no relationship just yet, and Caroline wasn't certain if she even wanted one. In order to find out, she and Matthew would have to get to know one another without talk of proxy fights and takeovers to set them at odds.

As she lay in bed that Friday night, she mocked the direction of her thoughts. Was she really the same woman who had sworn to exclude men from her life—the woman who would never again trust a man with her love or even her affection? It had been easy enough to make those vows when she was sure no man could ever tempt her to break them. She was probably a fool to go out with someone like Lyle, an unyielding businessman who had taken over company after company—and woman after woman. Somehow Caroline could not believe that the charming man she had met on Thursday could be the same person as the cold creature in all those newspaper photographs.

This breathless infatuation both confused and disturbed her, and on Saturday morning she sought escape in the sheer joy of running and jumping and shooting. Two hours of basketball and a long stroll in the afternoon helped relieve some of Caroline's tension. She looked forward to her date with Matthew Lyle both nervously and eagerly; she would pretend to herself that she was plain Carrie McKay—and try to remember that he was as dangerous as he was fascinating.

Her feminine instincts teased her into selecting a glamorous designer original to wear: a silk organza print in shades of brown, beige, and blue. The long-sleeved gown had a V neck, plunging back, and full skirt. After applying her usual light coat of makeup, Caroline automatically started to pin up her hair. Her hands dropped. Clay had always insisted that she looked too young and frivolous with a wavy mass of silvery hair cascading all over her shoulders. But Clay was gone now, and she could do as she pleased. She removed the hairpins, ran a brush through the freed locks, and went to the hall closet.

After slipping into a brown wool coat and matching gloves, she climbed up the driveway to the road. Several expensive cars whizzed by, Caroline glancing at the drivers as they passed. At first, when she spotted Matthew Lyle's car, she dismissed it and looked down the road for the next vehicle. After all, it was a moderately priced American model, several years old, with a dent near the front left headlight. But as the automobile slowed she looked again and noticed Matthew at the wheel.

He stopped the car, got out, and walked around to help her into her seat. Caroline found the gesture to be both chivalrous and seductive—his hand had lingered under her elbow longer than was strictly necessary. When he slid back into the driver's seat, she risked teasing, "With all your money, I expected at least a Mercedes. Maybe even a Rolls."

He shrugged. "Cars don't interest me. Boats interest me. I have three of them. Companies with healthy cash flows interest me. In fact, I collect them." Then he smiled in that crooked way of his and subjected Caroline to one of his intent gazes. "Also beautiful women, Carrie," he added softly.

"And do you collect *those,* too, Mr. Lyle?" she asked, her face warming with annoyance at the male chauvinism of that last line.

"No." He grinned, suddenly looking boyish. "But they've been known to collect *me!*"

Caroline forgave him his arrogance. No snappy retort came to mind, and besides, her body was broadcasting a demand that she stop resisting his appeal. She settled back into her seat as Matthew started the engine.

Their conversation as they drove was for the most part impersonal, although Matthew did ask Caroline what she did with her time. She told him that she was a graduate student and that she lived with her parents, who were out with friends that evening. To her relief, he soon switched to safer subjects, and over dinner they agreed that the Pacific Northwest was beautiful country, that the latest exhibition at the Seattle Museum's Modern Art Pavilion was intriguing, and that one of the best ways to spend an evening was at the theater. Caroline ate every bit of her shrimp scampi and found herself relaxing in Matthew's company. His rugged virility provoked an unfamiliar response from her body, but since he neither flirted openly with her nor touched her, she felt quite safe with him.

She had never experienced the unpressured high school and college dating that most young women take for granted and enjoyed her masquerade as an unworldly graduate student. She was in no hurry to tell him who she was; it was a heady feeling to watch those brown eyes turn warm and intent when he studied her face. She was afraid that if he discovered her true identity only hard, cold stares would come her way.

The opera, performed by a visiting company, was Mozart's delightful *Marriage of Figaro*. As they left the theater and walked across the street to retrieve the car from the Seattle Center garage, Caroline was humming the theme from the overture to herself. She hadn't felt so carefree in years, except on a basketball court, and when Matthew pointed to a spot on the front seat only inches from his own body, she was too happy to bother being nervous. She obediently slid over, resting her head on his shoulder when his arm dropped down to pull her close. As long as he was driving, she told herself, nothing could happen.

He stopped in front of her driveway and switched off the engine. Caroline straightened up, her pulse rate jumping at the sudden intimacy of the situation. "Thank you for a lovely evening, Matthew," she said, meaning every word of the conventional expression of appreciation. "I had . . ."

"It's not over yet. Invite me in for coffee," he interrupted in a husky voice.

Caroline's common sense overruled her craving to feel his mouth capture her own. Such an invitation would be far too dangerous. "I don't think . . ." she began.

But Matthew had already opened the door and was motioning her out his side. "I'll walk you down the hill then," he said. Caroline heard no note of passion in his offer, only politeness. She was perversely disappointed.

The drive plunged down the hillside to the garage of Clay Spencer's dramatic contemporary home. She still thought of the house as his, perhaps always would. Caroline allowed Matthew to take her arm and support her. It might be unliberated of her, but she liked the fact that he was so much taller than she was. It made her feel protected. At the doorway, he took her house key from her unresisting fingers and unlocked the door himself, stepping inside the front hall before she had a chance to protest.

Matthew closed the door. Caroline hurriedly clicked on the light, now acutely aware that she was alone with an experienced wolf only yards away from a queen-sized bed. After his easygoing manner all evening, this suddenly aggressive behavior had caught her off guard.

"I'll make the coffee," she murmured, starting toward the staircase.

The lower floor of the house was almost level with Lake Washington and contained a kitchen, living/dining room, and two bedrooms. The far end of the front hall, where they now stood, was railed for safety and looked out over the living room below. Nine-foot-high windows provided a spectacular view of the lake. The only other upstairs room was a small den, to the left.

Matthew put an arm around Caroline's waist to halt her progress. "Don't bother. Neither of us wants coffee," he said. His mouth settled on top of hers, moving lightly on her lips, then lifting. This unthreatening yet seductive caress sent ripples of heat shuddering through Caroline's body. As Matthew's lips wandered over her face, his other hand occupied itself with the task of unbuttoning her coat.

Caroline stood submissively still, neither cooperating with his overture nor rebuffing it. She allowed him to help her out of her coat and watched him shrug off his own. He walked into the den, tossed the coats over a convenient chair, and then started back to the hall. Caroline followed him with wary eyes, twisting her fingers together to hide the tremor in her hands.

Her own experience with men was practically nonexistent. Her few dates in high school had been awkward, adolescent encounters ending in clumsy good-night kisses. It had never occurred to her to be unfaithful to Clay during their marriage, even though they had no physical relationship. And those four and a half years with her husband had left her far too frightened of being hurt to risk involvements with any other men.

But Matthew Lyle had stimulated some long-dormant part of her nature into a full-blown eruption, and she was powerless to cool the internal explosion.

As he approached, she turned to the railing and gripped it fiercely. The moment he put his hands on her waist, however, she jerked around, skittish with tension. He backed her against the railing, his body very close to hers, not quite touching, and fondled a strand of her hair. Then he looped it behind her ear and bent his head, his lips cool and firm against her neck.

She shivered, embarrassed because her nervousness must be obvious to him. "You *are* jumpy," he whispered into her ear. "How long has it been, Carrie?"

The question was clearly a rhetorical one. Had Matthew had any interest in a reply he would not have turned her face up to his lips, his mouth stroking hers persuasively, intensifying the already hot flame inside of her. Caroline's hands crept around his waist, and before she could protest she found herself pressed firmly against his body, his hands pressing her to him, making her aware of every hard muscle. Her lips were parted with punishing swiftness, her mouth probed and explored with passionate impatience.

It was the first time Caroline had been kissed by a man with any real experience and technique. Matthew had gone too fast—demanded more than she could give—and initially she froze, her body objecting by means of a sudden, shocked stiffness. Her hands slid up to push against his chest, rejecting his rough invasion of her mouth. Although he loosened his hold, he refused to release her. His mouth became gentle and persuasive again, caressing, nibbling, teasing relentlessly.

Caroline heard her own soft moans as she began to kiss him back. Now when he parted her lips the intimate feel of his tongue moving against her own was arousing rather than alarming. And when he deepened the kiss into a passionate conquest, Caroline was only too ready to be enslaved.

She arched against him, and, her arms crept up around his neck. When Matthew gently lifted his head to break off the embrace, she withdrew her arms in confusion and looked up at him defensively. Had her inexperience been so obvious that she had disappointed him?

"I'm not going to make love to you in the middle of a hallway, Carrie," he said hoarsely. "Let's go down to the bedroom."

That blunt announcement brought Caroline crashing out of her fantasy world. Good grief, the man must assume that she did this sort of thing all the time. She should have known that when Matthew Lyle took a woman into his arms he didn't intend to stop after a few hot kisses.

"We—we hardly know each other," she stuttered, taking a few awkward steps to the side.

"Give me an hour, and you won't be able to say that," he shot back, apparently amused by her resistance.

"Matthew, I don't—I'm not the type of woman . . ."

". . . who goes in for one-night stands," he finished for her. "I don't either, Carrie." He ran his hands over her hair and down to her shoulders, then pulled her back into his arms. His lips started to rediscover her face, finally settling on the vulnerable spot just below her ear and nuzzling her skin in a way that made her burn for something far more intimate. "I won't hurt you, Carrie," he murmured. "Tonight, tomorrow night, next week—what's the point of making both of us wait?"

His lips sought hers again, and somehow Caroline's common sense won a battle with her inflamed senses. She turned her head away, so that his mouth grazed her cheek instead. Why did this man arouse such a wild physical response in her? It was laughable to remember that she had once believed herself incapable of such feelings.

"My parents . . ." she said, flustered. "They'll be home soon."

"No they won't." His hands dropped to his sides, his brown eyes so intent that Caroline colored and looked away. She turned her back to him and walked into the den. Matthew followed, snapping on a lamp that sat on one of the end tables.

He was suddenly so cool that the passionate lover of only moments ago might never have existed. Caroline watched in puzzlement as he strolled over to a display case and picked up a trophy—one of the awards she had won in intramural basketball.

"Basketball?" he asked lazily. "You don't seem the type. I would have bet you didn't know the difference between the spike on a track shoe and the one on a railroad tie."

There was a sarcastic note in his voice now that made Caroline extremely wary. "I'm very good," she answered. "I play with men—I mean, on a men's team."

But the correction to her unintentional double entendre came too late to ward off Matthew Lyle's unpleasant laughter. Caroline had the oddest sensation of being stalked. The man wanted to back her into a corner and then pounce, and his abrupt hostility confused her.

"Mind if I look around the house? It's very striking—if you happen to like contemporary architecture." His tone said that he preferred something more traditional.

Caroline, out of her depth and increasingly nervous in his presence, led him downstairs to the living room. He paused in front of the picture window and stared out at Lake Washington for several moments. "Daddy must make a good living," he commented. "What does he do to pay the mortgage?"

Caroline could manage only one word. "Electronics," she said in a vaguely strangled voice, her face turning pink. Matthew Lyle must have figured out who she was. It was the only explanation for his harshness. And his next statement confirmed it.

"You know something? You're a lousy liar, Mount Carrie. That *is* what your frustrated admirers call you, isn't it?"

Lake Washington became suddenly fascinating to Caroline. She stared out the window, willing herself to be cool and self-assured. She had already made a total fool of herself over this man, and the only way to salvage the situation was to pretend that it had all been a lighthearted game to her.

"Yes," she said with a smile. "That's what they call me. But it was fun being little Carrie McKay for one evening."

Matthew Lyle walked over to the cushioned sofa and leaned lazily back against the pillows, his feet sprawled out in front of him. He had no right to make himself at home in her house, and Caroline ached to order him off the premises. But not a trace of her anger was visible on her face as she seated herself in an armchair.

"I don't think you were acting," Matthew announced. "You were nervous tonight. And you didn't kiss me like a woman who's only pretending to enjoy something."

He was much too perceptive, Caroline thought to herself, but she'd never admit that he was right. "I'm a better actress than you give me credit for," she said aloud. "You're not the only one who plays cat and mouse with people."

An easy grin spread over his face. "You still think you bumped into me by accident?" he asked, his tone implying that Caroline was incredibly naive. "Not a chance, Carrie. I knew you'd go to the trade show, so I had one of my security men wait outside your office building. He tailed you to Seattle Center, then called me. I got there before you even came down from the Space Needle."

Caroline's tenuous composure turned tail and fled. "I don't understand," she said, disturbed by his statement and unable to disguise it.

"You wanted to meet with me, didn't you? Your secretary phoned at least twice for an appointment." He paused. "Why didn't you come up to me at the Kingdome? You stared hard enough, Carrie!"

His tone was mercilessly taunting. Caroline all but writhed with mortification. The man had been playing with her for weeks, refusing to see her in order to pique her interest and then setting up an "accidental" meeting so he would have the advantage of surprise. Her impulsive charade had played right into his hands. Good heavens, suppose she had let him take her to bed? She winced to imagine the look in his eyes the following morning.

There was no way to brazen her way out of this situation; all she could do was end it. She rose from her chair and said, in her most dismissive voice, "Please leave now, Mr. Lyle. You've had your fun."

"Wrong. I haven't even begun yet, Mrs. Spencer. Aren't you going to offer to negotiate with me?"

Caroline felt like moaning aloud as she dropped back into the seat. No matter what her personal feelings were toward Matthew Lyle—and she was both furious and deeply humiliated—she was still the president of

Elliot Bay Electronics, and the man sitting across from her still had the power to force the company into a bitter proxy fight.

"All right, yes," she replied coldly. "We intend to do everything in our power to fight your takeover attempt, and we're going to win. It would be beneficial to both of us if you would sell out. We're prepared to ask the stockholders to approve a very generous offer for your stock."

He shook his head, that lazy smile still on his mouth. "No way, Mount Carrie. Try again."

Caroline, enraged by his taunting sarcasm, clenched her fists in an effort to keep her voice level. "Very well, Mr. Lyle. The board of directors has authorized me to offer you or anyone of your choice a seat on our board. I suggest you accept. If you insist on running your own slate of directors at the annual meeting, you'll lose."

"Wrong again," he needled. "*If* I decide I want your company, I'll take it. You won't win. I will."

"The word "if" had been lightly emphasized, prompting Caroline to fix glacial blue eyes on her tormentor. "If?" she repeated icily.

"Your company appeals to me, Carrie, but I've found something that appeals to me even more. I'm a fairly straightforward guy. The game we played tonight was your idea, not mine." He paused, as though waiting for some remark from Caroline, but she maintained a tight-lipped silence.

Then he continued with businesslike crispness, "Spend a weekend with me at my place in the San Juans, and I'll settle for two seats on the board of directors and an immediate audit of the books. In return, I give you my word that I won't take any further action for twelve months."

Caroline was absolutely livid by now. Who did the

man think he was, toying with her, making love to her, and then propositioning her outrageously? And what did he take her for? A piece of high-class merchandise that he could purchase at his whim? Naturally he would own a love nest in the San Juans, those picturesque islands some eighty miles northwest of Seattle. All the best wolves did!

When she thought of her unbridled response to his kisses, she wanted to crawl under the nearest chair. "Get out of here," she said furiously, every effort at restraint abandoned. "I'd throw up if I let you touch me again."

Matthew stood up, his anger apparent now in his stiffly held body. "That comment is going to cost you, Mount Carrie," he said harshly. "When you change your mind—and you *will* change your mind—you can come to my office and politely ask to see me. And if I decide to let you in, you'd better make sure you ask me *very* nicely if the offer is still good."

Without another word, he stalked up the stairs and out of the house, slamming the door behind him. Caroline had never seen a man so incensed, and she was shaking long after he drove away.

Chapter Four

"Lyle filed with the S.E.C. yesterday." Sam Hanover had just walked briskly into Caroline's office and now stood on the other side of her desk, announcing this news in a curt tone that seemed simultaneously to blame her for the situation and ask her what she was going to do about it.

Caroline took a deep breath and slowly exhaled, determined to slow the accelerating tempo of her heartbeats. She had expected Lyle to make a move—he had been furious with her when he left on Saturday—so there was no reason to let the news upset her. The only surprise was that he had waited until yesterday, Tuesday, to declare his intention to fight for control of the company.

On Monday morning, Caroline had stopped by Sam's office to tell him that she had spoken to Lyle over the weekend. She mentioned that Lyle had refused both a seat on the board and her offer to buy him out, and that he seemed totally confident about his ability to win a proxy fight. She had not felt it necessary to add just what terms the man *was* willing to accept.

"I think you'd better sit down and talk this out with me, Sam," she said. Once the older man had pulled the chair opposite her desk around to the side and dropped into it, she continued, "We'll fight him." Her voice was level and assured, the prospect of doing battle with Matthew Lyle didn't send shivers of apprehension rippling down her back. "We always knew it would come to this."

"Talk to him again, Carrie. Maybe he'll reconsider," Sam urged.

She shook her head. "There's no point to it, Sam. You're the one who's always telling me to face facts. Well, the fact is that we're a prime target for a takeover attempt. You're the one who taught me about things like that. Why wouldn't Lyle want EBE? Our stock is undervalued and the shareholders will jump at the chance to get Olympia stock that sells for almost double the price of ours. In a year we'll be swimming in cash from government contracts, and Lyle can't wait to get his hands on some of that money to finance his other investments. Then there's our low corporate debt—less money he'll have to worry about paying off." But even as she mouthed the conventional reasons as to why the firm had become a target for a corporate buccaneer like Matthew Lyle, she knew that the man's motives were a good deal more complex.

In the beginning perhaps his only interest had been in possessing Elliot Bay Electronics. But now, for some obscure, illogical reason of his own, he seemed intent on possessing Caroline Spencer as well. When she had rejected him, his fury had been dauntingly apparent, and Caroline was baffled by the intensity of his response.

Judging from his taunts on Saturday night, he didn't even like her. Was his anger due to physical frustration? It seemed doubtful. After all, he had his choice of women. Or was he like all the others, challenged by her cool image? Did he imagine himself as the man who could make a dormant volcano blaze into life? That made no sense either, because she had been anything but cool in Matthew's arms. From the wanton way she had responded, he had ample reason to think she was his for the taking.

"Okay, you're right." Sam's admission forced Caroline to turn her attention to their immediate problem. "We'll have to hire a proxy hunter," he went on. "We can't do this on our own."

A proxy hunter, Caroline knew, made a business of cadging votes for whichever side was willing to pay him the most money. But she had no personal knowledge of such people. "I want to hire the best," she said. "Who would that be?"

"I don't think the best would be available in this case." Sam Hanover permitted himself a humorless smile. "When it comes to rustling up votes, nobody's more of an expert than Joe Symington."

"Matthew Lyle's cousin and chief henchman. I can't say I'm surprised. The man's obviously had plenty of practice," Caroline said acidly.

Sam nodded. "He's been with Lyle almost every step of the way—sold his own business to Olympia for a few million dollars and a senior vice-presidency. It was the best deal Lyle ever made. Not only can Symington talk an impoverished widow out of her last dime, he's a fantastic corporate bloodhound, Carrie. He has a nose for shady deals. I don't want him sniffing around EBE."

Caroline frowned, taken aback by the vehemence in Sam's tone. "Really?" she asked coolly.

"I wasn't suggesting he would find anything irregular. I just don't like the idea of standing around at attention while the guy examines the books with a high-powered microscope."

Caroline understood Sam Hanover's feelings. Her imagination conjured up a picture of herself running to do Matthew Lyle's bidding, and she knew that the prospect of playing errand boy for Joseph Symington would be equally distasteful to Sam. So she smiled sympathetically and asked him if he knew of anyone else who had a reputation for winning proxy fights.

He named a California firm that specialized in that business, and two days later one of the company's partners flew up to Seattle to talk to Caroline, Sam, and the other members of the board of directors. After a three-hour meeting during which he examined company records, freely questioned the board, and dissected the firm's situation, he declared that he was not sanguine about the prospect of taking on Matthew Lyle.

"I'm going to be straight with you people," he told them. "The first thing we usually do in a case like this is to investigate the guy behind the takeover. If we can dig up enough evidence of business losses or questionable practices we can usually discredit him with the shareholders. But Lyle is clean. We've gone up against him once before, and the only thing we could uncover was a rumor about an affair with the secretary to the president of a company he was after. Maybe he did use her to get information, but they were both over twenty-one. Nobody cares about Lyle's private life. It's even an asset with some of the male stockholders—the rogue male image. When it comes to business, the guy's got credibility to burn. Olympia Industries is extremely well managed. The best I can say is that I think you'll go into your annual meeting with a fighting chance. Most of your big stockholders won't sign proxies. It's doubtful that Lyle can get fifty-one percent of the votes nailed down in advance, but unfortunately, neither can you, even with the head start you've got."

The board had accepted this assessment and hired the firm to manage EBE's end of the proxy fight. Unable to attack Lyle on the basis of previous takeover campaigns, they had to rely on a show of confidence and a staunch defense of management decisions made by the present board.

As EBE's "hired gun" had predicted, many shareholders decided to attend the annual meeting rather than sign away their votes to either side. But Matthew Lyle claimed that the campaign was going exceptionally well, and given the appeal of his promises, Caroline could hardly question his figures.

What most distressed her was Lyle's plan for the disposition of her company. He stated blandly that once Olympia Industries owned EBE, he would probably sell off the less lucrative, nonmilitary division of the firm, ploughing the profits back into the electronic weapons division. He thus intended to liquidate the original division of the company—the very part Caroline truly cared about. She wished that she had the capital to simply buy it back from him, but knew that even if she raised the money he would never make a deal with *her*.

During the next three weeks Elliot Bay Electronics stock rose eight more points, as each side sought to buy every share that became available. Caroline was soon weary of giving interviews to business reporters—reporters who persisted in rudely reminding her that Matthew Lyle was winning this corporate war. She smiled her disagreement, her features invariably cool and her voice utterly confident.

A second session with the Los Angeles proxy hunter confirmed that the outlook for EBE was not promising. "Our best information says that thirteen to fifteen percent of the proxies were returned, and Lyle is getting two-thirds of the votes. At this point you control about thirty-five percent of the stock and he controls about twenty-five percent. It's obvious that the issue will be decided at your annual meeting. I've felt out the major shareholders and too many of them are leaning toward Lyle's deal. In all honesty, I have to recommend that you reopen your negotiations with a view toward a friendly acquisition. You'll end up with better terms."

Although Matthew Lyle's proposition had haunted Caroline's nights for three and a half weeks, she continued to mentally reject that cold-blooded ultimatum. Now she sat and listened to the proxy hunter's report, and it was apparent both to her and to everyone else in the room that Lyle was going to snatch away the company.

As the board considered its next move, Caroline could sense that sentiment had shifted toward accepting an acquisition. Terms were discussed. Sam Hanover insisted that there must be no interference by Olympia Industries in the management of EBE. Several board members pointed out that Lyle would never agree to such a condition. Ultimately, the board instructed Caroline to offer to drop the company's opposition to a takeover, provided that the present management and corporate structure be retained for a period of twenty-one months—until the end of the next calendar year.

Caroline excused herself to make the call, hoping to get the matter settled while the board was still in session. She sat and stared at the phone for several long minutes before picking up the receiver. Given Matthew's angry words about coming to his office and begging for an interview, she doubted he would even speak to her.

To her surprise he came on the line almost immediately, interrupting her cool hello with the words, "You sure know how to make a guy suffer, Carrie. Have you finally decided to stop fighting me?"

Caroline ignored both the caress in his voice and the double meaning of his question and relayed the terms of the board's offer in a businesslike voice.

"What about *my* offer," was the soft reply. When Caroline hesitated, unable to find a suitable retort to that, he went on, "Forget the part about cooling your heels outside my office, Carrie. I was angry when I said that. You let me kiss you and touch you until you were practically purring. You had to know how badly I wanted you. But the minute I said so, you backed off. You started handing out phony excuses about parents who don't exist and told me the whole thing was a game to you. I don't like being teased." He paused for a moment, then concluded huskily, "I'm not angry anymore, Carrie. And I still want to make love to you."

Caroline swallowed nervously, embarrassed by the validity of his complaint and frightened by the hunger in his voice. She had never meant to be a sexual tease. Although she had fended off numerous advances in the last year, no man in her experience had been as blunt as Matthew Lyle, and she had no idea how to cope with him. She could only disregard his comments and hope he would drop the whole topic.

"Do I take it that you're rejecting our offer, Mr. Lyle?" she asked.

"What are you so afraid of, Carrie?"

Any further discussion with the man was useless. It was obvious that he was only too accustomed to success with women and considered her a sophisticated widow who was fair game. He had no way of knowing that she couldn't handle a brief affair, no matter how loud he had made her purr on that Saturday night. His record in taking over women might be just as dazzling as his record in taking over companies, but Caroline McKay Spencer told herself firmly that she was going to be the one who got away.

"Goodbye, Mr. Lyle," she said politely, hanging up the phone before he could reply.

She took a few minutes to control the tremor in her body, then walked back to the boardroom and told the members that Lyle had refused to consider anything but a complete takeover. Of me, she added silently.

Most of those in the room accepted his decision philosophically. Why should the man settle for anything less when it was apparent that he was going to win?

Sam Hanover was the one exception. He exerted such intense pressure on Caroline to resolve the corporate struggle amicably that a few days later, in the beginning of April, she went down to his office, intent on finding out why he was so much more adamant than the others.

"I'm sixty years old, Carrie. I've given the best years of my life to this company. No one else is going to hire me if Lyle throws me out," he told her.

Caroline was astonished by this speech. "With your

experience and knowledge? Of course they will, Sam," she replied.

He looked her straight in the eye, and Caroline could hardly fail to notice how very bleak his expression was. "There's something else, isn't there, Sam?" she asked.

"I could go to jail for fraud, Carrie."

The statement left her speechless. She had been sitting down, her hands gripping the arms of the chair, her heart pounding harshly against her rib cage.

"I made illegal payments—bribes, Carrie—but Clay was determined to have those contracts. The deal was made before he died, but the payoffs started just after you became president. The expenditures aren't listed as bribes, of course," he added dryly. "They're buried in the books under several other columns. Our auditors will never catch them. What they do is too superficial. Even if Lyle calls in his own C.P.A.'s I wouldn't worry. But if Symington takes an interest, we're finished. He likes to analyze spending patterns. He has a nose for fraud and he's going to realize something is fishy. He'll dissect this company, and before we turn around he'll have the S.E.C. on our tail."

Caroline was no longer merely incapable of speech—she was stunned. It was true that Clay Spencer had been a driven man before his death, but she had never imagined that his irrationality would extend to the point of breaking the law.

When she finally snapped out of her dazed state, she managed to murmur, "The S.E.C. . . . even if they investigate, they'll only slap our wrists and fine us. They don't . . ."

"There's a new commissioner, Carrie. Remember? He's out to crack down on this sort of thing. He'll turn the results of the investigation over to the U.S. Attorney's office. I can't face a trial—possibly even a jail sentence. You've got to try again."

The way his eyes traveled over her body disturbed her. She knew he was suggesting seduction, but somehow that didn't shock her. Sam was a desperate man.

If Clay's activities—and those of Sam Hanover—ever became public knowledge, the scandal would ruin Clay's name forever. At the moment that seemed even more important to Caroline than the question of whether or not Sam went to prison. She had dedicated four and a half years of her life to her late husband, and if bribery charges ruined his reputation, the sacrifice she had made would be an empty one.

"I may be able to do something," she muttered. Without another word, she left his office.

It was impossible for Caroline to do any work that day. She had been unhappy in her marriage to Clay Spencer, but she recognized that she could have left him at any time. She had stayed to repay his affection and kindness—to protect him from himself—and had never blamed him for the fact that his illness had affected his mind. She was frequently miserable, but had never felt trapped.

Now she did. Contrary to Matthew's supposition, she wasn't really afraid of *him*. She was more afraid of herself. The woman who had responded with such abandon was a stranger to her.

She thought she understood Matthew's behavior. When he wanted a company, conquest became an obsession. He wasn't satisfied until he safely possessed it. Then he lost interest and mounted the next campaign.

To him, Caroline Spencer was no different from the companies on his "hit list." He wanted her because she had proved elusive, a challenge. He was enjoying the pursuit. He would probably find the actual takeover far less satisfying.

Even so, she knew he would be anything but cold or cruel when he made love to her, and that was part of the problem. Even if she could cope with the whole concept of a weekend affair, she could never deal with the subsequent pain. Matthew would see that she responded, but afterward she would want to die of shame.

Yet what choice did she have? Could she really allow Clay's name to be ruined? Could she bear to see her company torn apart in the newspapers and an important corporate officer, a friend, sent to jail? Suppose the revelations led to canceled contracts? People slept together all the time. Maybe she was making a fuss over nothing.

Finally, desperately in need of some advice, Caroline asked Maggie to have dinner with her that evening. Since she trusted Maggie completely, it was easy to explain to her that Sam had used company funds for illegal purposes. But Caroline's face turned a dusky pink as she began to relate the events of that Saturday night over a month before and was red by the time she got to Lyle's outrageous proposition and her own angry reaction to it.

She concluded her account by telling Maggie about her call to Lyle a few mornings earlier. "He wouldn't even deal with the board's offer, Maggie. He kept making personal comments. He accused me of being a tease, leading him on. I never meant to do that. Then he said that he wasn't angry anymore, that he still wanted to make love to me." She shuddered. "His voice—it was almost as if he already had me in bed. I hung up on him."

"I don't understand you, Caroline," Maggie replied between rapid forkfuls of her crabmeat salad. "There are very few women in Seattle who would turn down a secluded weekend with Matthew Lyle. Most of them would be flattered to death at the way he's chasing you. You admit he turns you on, so what's the problem? It's true that things weren't easy for you with Clay, but that's no reason to run away from every other man you meet. At worst, you'll have a terrific weekend. At best . . . who knows?"

Naturally Maggie would express that point of view, Caroline thought dejectedly. She had slept with Jerry the same week she met him. Their relationship had deepened afterward, but she saw nothing wrong with letting an intense attraction lead quickly into bed.

Besides, Caroline had omitted one crucial piece of information. And without it Maggie would never understand why Caroline was so wary of Lyle and why his behavior had her so panicked. "I never slept with Clay, Maggie," she said quietly.

"You never—you mean, nothing? No sex at all?" Maggie blurted out, clearly astonished. "But why? I mean, why not?"

Caroline had no choice but to explain why she had married Clay Spencer and to describe the horrible last few years with him. She had never confided such personal details to anyone, and she made Maggie swear to keep every word of it to herself. "I didn't hate Clay—somehow I couldn't even blame him. He was sick, Maggie, and he needed me to protect him. But it scarred me. I still have nightmares sometimes. I dream I'm still married to him and I wake up shaking."

"Oh, Caroline! No wonder you keep men at a distance! Maybe if you explained . . ." Maggie paused when Caroline shook her head bleakly. "No, I suppose

71

not. Matthew Lyle is very determined. Even if he believed you, he wouldn't let a little obstacle like virginity stop him. He might even like the idea."

She was silent for several moments, apparently weighing Caroline's alternatives, then straightened up, put down her fork, and said crisply, "All right, Caroline. I won't presume to give you advice, but if you want help in making a decision, I can try to provide it. You can refuse Lyle's invitation but if you do he's going to take over the company and sell off the only part you care about. Joe Symington will probably uncover the payoffs Sam made, in which case there may be an investigation and a scandal. Eventually it will blow over. My guess is that a good lawyer will keep Sam out of jail. As far as Clay's reputation goes, I think you're a saint to let it trouble you, given what you went through with him."

"Maggie, you don't understand. For years, Clay took care of me, and I . . ."

"I *do* understand," Maggie interrupted, "but Clay is dead and you're alive. In the end you'll be a very wealthy young woman. You'll find something else to do with your life—something you'll enjoy."

She paused only briefly before launching into the opposite argument. "On the other hand, if you agree to spend the weekend with Lyle, I think you'll be able to persuade him to keep Symington away from the company's books. You have quite an effect on men, Caroline, and Lyle's just the latest in a long line. I think he's infatuated enough to give you anything you want, and besides, one small company can't mean that much to him. In a year you'll be able to get the company into such good shape that the shareholders won't be interested in acquisitions or mergers. You can vote Lyle off the board once you're in control and keep Symington away permanently. Whether you go through with it or not depends on how important Sam, Clay, and EBE are to you."

She paused again, continuing rather more delicately, "Just remember that when you go to bed with someone, Caroline, you don't have to give him your soul, and you don't have to sacrifice your independence. I know that's important to you. You'll be giving Matthew Lyle your body for forty-eight hours—nothing more. From what you've told me, you'll probably enjoy doing it. Afterward, you can refuse to see him again, if that's what you want. There's no reason to become emotionally involved with him."

Caroline was torn between admiration and repulsion. Maggie was telling her that she could use her body to get whatever she wanted out of Lyle, then casually drop him when she was through with him. She had never pictured herself as a femme fatale, although people implied that she was beautiful enough. She didn't believe in using people, no matter how altruistic the reason.

But then, Lyle had no qualms about using her! So why did she hesitate?

"Part of me wishes I could do it, Maggie," she said, sighing. "But I just don't think I can."

Maggie shrugged and changed the subject to dessert. Matthew Lyle's name was not mentioned again.

That night, Caroline had another of her nightmares. She was a student again, and Clay Spencer was berating her, making her feel miserably guilty because she had gotten a "C" on an important exam. In her dream all her repressed anger exploded. As she screamed at

Clay, he slowly turned into Sam Hanover. He clutched at his chest and fell to the floor, and Caroline woke up covered with a film of perspiration.

Without Sam, she never would have succeeded as EBE president. How could she risk sending him to jail for something Clay had forced on him? And Clay . . . Clay had been ill, not at all himself, those last few years. Besides, wasn't there a part of *her* that was terrified by the idea of losing the presidency of EBE? As long as she was the boss, nobody could run her life for her.

All during the next day carefully buried memories kept surfacing—memories of how she used to endure Clay's tantrums. She had learned to detach herself from her own emotions, as though she were standing off to one side, watching Clay Spencer browbeat some other woman. Eventually, he no longer had the power to hurt her. If she could do that with Clay, she could do it with Matthew Lyle, too. Maggie was right. There was no reason to become emotionally involved with the man. He was exerting unethical pressure on her, giving her no real option to refuse, and she would simply have to think of the whole thing as a business deal. Under the circumstances, she had no need to feel ashamed.

By late afternoon Caroline had decided to go see Matthew Lyle in person. She was instinctively repelled by the idea of conducting such personal business on the phone. As she rode the bus to his office, she had to keep reminding herself that she could always change her mind. It would cost her nothing to go up to the San Juan Islands with him, because if she found that she couldn't go through with it, she could walk out of his cabin and find a place to stay in town. He wouldn't drag her into bed—he was hardly the type to engage in rape.

When she gave her name to his receptionist, the

young woman exclaimed with an unworldly smile, "Oh, yes, Mrs. Spencer! Everyone's talking about you. Mr. Lyle mentioned you'd probably come around this week. He's in with Mr. Symington at the moment, but if you would like to take a seat, he'll be out in a few minutes."

Caroline walked over to the cream-colored couch. The man had actually been egotistical enough to take her surrender for granted! The idea of it made her seethe with resentment. She sat down and picked up a copy of *Architectural Digest,* only pretending to look at the pictures. In fact, she was forcing herself to cool down so that she would be controlled and businesslike during the coming interview. Maybe she could even persuade Lyle to change his mind about the whole thing.

He walked out of his office ten minutes later, immersed in conversation with the man by his side. When he spotted Caroline, he cocked an eyebrow inquiringly. She stood, her body taut with tension, and resolved that she would not say a single word until they were alone together.

"Joe, I'm sure you recognize Carrie Spencer," Matthew said easily. "Carrie, this is my cousin, Joe Symington."

Caroline offered her hand. She knew that Joe Symington was in his middle forties, but he looked much younger. He was shorter than Matthew by a few inches, his frame lean and fit, his hair as dark as his cousin's. He shook her hand warmly and smiled at her, his blue eyes openly sympathetic. For a man reputed to be a ruthless proxy hunter and corporate ferret, he seemed remarkably unferocious.

"I'll look forward to knowing you better," he said.

Caroline was spared the necessity of answering by

Matthew's "Come back as soon as you feel out Danforth, okay, Joe? We need to talk out where we stand on this one."

Joe Symington nodded as Matthew took Caroline's arm and escorted her into his office. He closed the door firmly behind them. When Caroline glanced up at him, his brown eyes were shining with amusement. "I'm glad you decided that I wouldn't make you sick," he drawled. "Now I won't have to spend all my time searching for a cure."

In spite of his husky, blunt manner on the phone, Caroline hadn't expected such an intense stare or those teasingly passionate words. She began to unbutton her coat, more to disguise the unsteadiness of her hands than because she actually wanted to remove it.

"Let me do it." Matthew turned her to face him, his fingers brushing away her own. "It's one of my favorite activities, unbuttoning buttons," he said with a grin.

Obviously the man had had plenty of practice. He slid the buttons through their respective buttonholes with deliberate ease, making Caroline feel that he was removing a garment far more intimate than an overcoat. She was relieved when he slipped the coat from her shoulders and walked over to an antique coat tree to hang it up. But a moment later he was walking back to her, standing behind her with his hands caressing her shoulders. When he ran them down the length of her arms and wrapped them around her waist, Caroline felt his touch burn right through the fabric of her long-sleeved, silk shirtwaist dress.

"I told you that I'd been thinking about you all last month," he said softly. "But now I'm thinking about this weekend. I'll be able to touch you any time I want to. Undress you. Make love to you over and over again." He bent his head and nuzzled her neck, his lips warm and disturbing against her bare skin.

Caroline was shocked that a burst of heat could sear her so intimately. This couldn't be happening to her—she couldn't be responding to his seductive voice and teasing mouth—not all over again! She wanted to keep her emotional distance from this man, not all but fall into his arms!

She forced herself to stiffen and said in a voice so icy he could have sculpted it, "You don't have to spell it out, Mr. Lyle. I understand my position perfectly."

Soft, deep laughter greeted the statement. "Mount Carrie—unapproachable and snow capped and beautiful—it's such an appropriate name for you when you try to freeze me off. But it won't work, Carrie. I can feel you trembling." He turned her in his arms, oblivious to the resistance she mounted, and lowered his mouth to hers.

Caroline's hands flew up to press against his chest. She had to put some space between them. His lips brushed hers and would have settled into a bruising possession had she not pleadingly objected, "Matthew, I came here to discuss *business!*"

He straightened, his hands still on her waist, and smiled down at her in that crookedly appealing way of his. "I haven't forgotten our deal. A weekend in the San Juans in exchange for two seats on the board, an outside audit of the books, and no further interference for a year. I'm giving up a lot for this; I expect a terrific weekend in exchange, Carrie."

She ignored the sparkle in his eyes. "Can't we come to some other . . . arrangement?"

"No."

He said the word so brusquely that Caroline knew

the situation was hopeless. Nonetheless, she persisted in a weak voice, "You won't change your mind?"

In reply, he pulled her into his arms, one hand splayed against the small of her back to press her close, the other holding her face. Several layers of clothing did nothing to mitigate the muscled hardness of his body as he kissed her, his tongue gently probing her mouth. On some level Caroline was ashamed of her own frenzied reaction, but she was powerless to control it. The seductive movements of her mouth and body ignited a fierce response in Matthew, who deepened the kiss into a wild ravishment and then all but flung himself away from her.

"Does it *feel* like I'm going to change my mind?" he muttered harshly.

It didn't. It felt like exactly the opposite, and Caroline had been so uninhibitedly enthusiastic in her response that Matthew had every right to assume she was just as eager as he was. She started to turn away, wanting only to hide the blush that had risen to her face, but Matthew caught her arm and forced her chin up. "Come home with me tonight, Carrie, and I'll settle for only *one* seat on the board," he drawled.

Caroline shook her head and shrugged away from him. She walked to the window and stared down at the traffic, but saw only a blur of colors. Could she really go through with this? When he touched her, her body caught fire, making a mockery of her intention to block off her emotions with this man. How could she accept that, when all these years she had thought of herself as practically frigid? She was terrified by his power to make her lose control of herself and mortified that she would respond so wantonly to a virtual stranger.

"Tell me about your marriage, Carrie."

Caroline hadn't heard Matthew's footsteps as he crossed the room to stand behind her. His tone demanded a straight answer, as though she were one of his subordinates.

Caroline slowly turned around, the frozen mask on her face no act. She had found it difficult to discuss Clay Spencer even with Maggie, whom she had known for over eleven years. She would never reveal anything about her marriage to Matthew Lyle. He was interested only in her body, and the more he found out about her, the more he would eventually hurt her.

Her silence appeared to irritate him. Or perhaps it was the expression on her face—her Mount Carrie expression. When he spoke again, his voice was icy. "You married a man three times your age. Why?"

"It's none of your business. Just because I agreed to sleep with you this weekend, that doesn't mean you own me," she answered just as icily.

"And suppose I want to *keep* sleeping with you? Then what happens?" he snapped out.

"Suppose *you* want? Everybody has to do what *you* want, is that it, Matthew?" Caroline stormed.

"I want to know what makes you tick. Was it his money, Carrie? Did you look forward to becoming a wealthy widow?"

"I'm not some kind of microscopic specimen! Don't try to dissect me!"

"Answer me, Carrie!"

Caroline was furious with his arrogant invasion of her privacy. "Believe what you want to! I won't discuss my marriage with you, Matthew, and that's final!"

"In other words, yes!" was the angry retort. "You must have celebrated for a week when old Clay finally cashed in his chips!"

The acid, totally inaccurate assessment of her motives stung, in spite of Caroline's attempt to slough it off. How many people believed that her motive for marrying Clay had been sheer avarice? She maintained a rigid silence. Better to be branded a gold digger than to defend herself to Matthew Lyle and leave herself open to future agony of a far worse sort.

"You're like a marble statue when you pull that Mount Carrie routine—beautiful, cold, perfect." He glanced at his watch. "If I didn't know that Joe was coming back here, I'd take it as a challenge. If you plan to try it at the cabin, don't bother; it doesn't impress me. I could have you begging for me within twenty seconds."

Caroline simply continued to stare at him, furious at his egotism and certain that he was wrong. She refused to believe that she was that wanton. She heard him mutter something under his breath, a frustrated, monosyllabic curse. Then he said impatiently, "I'll pick you up at your house at nine o'clock tomorrow morning, Carrie. Be on time. We'll stop at Pike Place Market, then drive up to Anacortes."

Caroline stood motionless, her arms at her sides, refusing to acknowledge Matthew's presence even when he approached to kiss her. She found his behavior sickening. How could he continue to regard her body with such lust when he disdained her soul? Why would he want to make love to a woman whom he so obviously believed to be mercenary, calculating, and cold-blooded?

His lips covered hers, his hands lightly holding her upper arms. "I don't want to fight with you, Carrie," he murmured against her mouth. When she failed to respond to the seductive way his lips were grazing her own, he sighed and released her.

"So much for your twenty seconds!" she spat out at him.

"Look, if I was wrong about you and Spencer, I'm sorry," he said, obviously exasperated. "How am I supposed to know *what* to think if you won't talk to me about it? It's not just idle curiosity—it matters to me."

Caroline was somehow relieved that he cared about what type of person she was, but still had no intention of answering his questions. She simply repeated, "I told you, it's none of your business."

"Right! I don't own you! I get the message!" He stalked away from her as though he might be tempted to strike her if he stayed too close.

Caroline said nothing. She walked over to the coat tree and fetched her coat, then started toward the door. She wasn't surprised when Matthew stopped her.

"Sit!" he said, pulling her over to the couch.

The command made her bristle, but she complied. He seemed angry enough to pick her up and dump her on the sofa if she tried to leave. She was no longer quite so infuriated with *him*. His apology had sounded sincere, and his frustration with her silence was only too evident. He probably wasn't accustomed to such stubbornness in those he dealt with. No doubt everyone jumped to do his bidding the moment he whistled.

He dropped down beside her and began to stroke her arm with gentle fingers. She looked straight ahead, trying to ignore him. "Are you coming with me tomorrow?" he asked huskily.

She didn't know what she was going to do. When he spoke in that tone of voice and touched her that way, she couldn't think rationally. Why couldn't she have stayed angry with him? "No," she answered. "I don't want to."

"Twenty minutes ago you wanted to. I could have

made love to you on the sofa. You're annoyed because I kept asking you about Spencer. So, okay, I admit it's probably none of my business. I won't badger you about it."

Somehow, Caroline thought, her decision had gotten all tangled up in personal considerations. She had to force herself to remember all her reasons for coming here today. If she left now, Matthew would be enraged. He would take his revenge on her and her company, tearing both of them to shreds like a wolf with a hapless rabbit.

His fingers strayed to the neckline of her dress, undoing the first of the buttons that ran down the bodice, sending tongues of flame through her veins. "Stop that!" she whispered, trying to ignore the devastating effect of his hand gently caressing her breasts.

"I've finally got your attention," he said with a satisfied look.

His hand slid around her back to pull her closer and he began to kiss her—light, fleeting, maddening passes at her mouth bestowed with the goal of making her moan for more.

"Matthew, no." The protest was considerably less than half-hearted. The more he teased, the less she could resist him. And when he opened his mouth to cajole her lips apart, she stopped trying. She found herself reveling in his impatience, his roughness. Her hands gripped the front of his jacket and she kissed him back just as wildly.

Suddenly the warm pressure of his mouth was withdrawn and he was staring intently at her, mesmerizing her with his gaze.

"Tomorrow at nine, Carrie?"

"Yes. Right." Anything to get out of this office. She needed time to think.

Matthew eased himself up from the couch, put his arm around her waist, and walked her to the door. He tucked a finger under her chin and stared down at her, that crooked smile on his lips. "I'll look forward to it," he told her. And she had no doubt about what he meant.

Chapter Five

That night, as Caroline packed for the weekend, it struck her that when she had decided to go to Matthew's office she had never dreamed he would want to spirit her away to the San Juans quite so precipitously. He was a busy man; she had unconsciously assumed he would schedule the trip in two or three weeks at the earliest. She had depended on having some time to think things over, to change her mind, but she had not reckoned with his apparently intense desire for her.

Could she really go through with this? By that afternoon she had convinced herself that her only motivations concerned Clay, and Sam, and keeping control of the company. Now she was not so sure. She had left Matthew's office less than five hours before, and she was already day dreaming about him. Surely all that anger must mean he felt something more for her than simple physical desire?

All the same, complete intimacy frightened her. She

suspected that the only reason she would be able to get in the car with Matthew Lyle the next morning was that she would be able to give him the slip that afternoon if she wanted to.

He had mentioned that they would be driving up to Anacortes, which was located on Fidalgo Island, some eighty miles north of Seattle. Caroline knew that one of Washington's many ferry lines ran from Anacortes west through the San Juans and on to Sidney, British Columbia, on Vancouver Island. The ferry stopped only at the major islands in the San Juans, none of which was exactly the wilderness. Given his wealth, Matthew Lyle's "cabin" was more likely some luxurious little vacation cottage, complete with heat in the winter, air conditioning in the summer, and the most modern of kitchens and baths. The nearest neighbor was probably down the street, the nearest town only a short stroll away. There was no reason to panic—she would be as safe with him in the San Juan Islands as she had been at the opera a month ago. And she would be able to get away from him whenever she wanted to.

The next morning she called her office and left a message with the receptionist that she would be away through Monday. She just didn't feel up to facing Maggie, despite the fact that she knew the other woman would support her in her decision. Then she pulled on designer corded blue jeans, a Pendleton wool workshirt, and a navy windbreaker. Her suitcase contained cosmetics, a pair of boots, two changes of clothing, and a pink and white flannel nightgown, which would probably appall the sophisticated Matthew Lyle if he ever saw her in it.

But Caroline was beginning to doubt that he would. She admitted to herself that she wanted to spend the day with him, but the night was another matter. She had difficulty picturing herself standing in front of him in her nightgown, which no doubt he would immediately begin to unbutton.

Perhaps in anticipation of a quiet weekend spent alone, she included several hard-cover novels she wanted to read. The suitcase was rather heavy when she picked it up and lugged it to the front door. She was less than one-third of the way up the drive when Matthew drove up. Seconds later he was trotting down to meet her, his body encased in closely fitting jeans and a sweat shirt.

He removed the case from her hand. "What have you got in here, Carrie? A blunt instrument to bludgeon me with in case you chicken out?" he asked with a smile.

"Books," she answered, not returning his cheerful look.

He shifted the case from his right hand to his left as they walked. "You should have waited for me to help you with this. You could have strained your back dragging it up the hill."

"Heaven forbid!" Caroline retorted. "I'm sure you want me in perfect shape for our weekend activities."

"Don't malign my motives," he said with a laugh. "Even if you strained your back we'd manage. Credit me with some imagination as a lover."

She didn't want to think about *what* kind of lover he was. His lighthearted gibe made her blush, both with embarrassment and nervousness. When they reached the car he opened the trunk and slid her case inside on top of his own. A cooler was wedged to one side, with several grocery bags lined up on the other.

As they drove downtown toward the Pike Place Market, he asked her, "What kinds of books? What do you like to read?"

Caroline supplied the titles. All were current best sellers, including the latest novel by an aggressively feminist author who had raked the male sex over the coals in her three previous books. The mention of the title elicited a groan from Matthew. "I'm not letting you near that one. By the time you've read two chapters, you'll probably throw it at me and lock me out of the cabin."

Caroline was disconcerted by his easygoing charm. He seemed to be thoroughly relaxed, just as though they were longtime lovers who had gone away for many such weekends together. It was only nine fifteen, hours and hours before they would even reach his cabin, yet her nerves were already as taut as a rope in a tug of war, with conflicting emotions pulling at her. She was unresponsive to Matthew's efforts at conversation, answering with brief, mumbled replies. The silence that resulted was even more uncomfortable for her.

A sports car pulled out of a parking space just half a block from the market as they were approaching. The vacant space looked no larger than Matthew's car, but he somehow managed to edge the vehicle into it. As they walked to what he told her was his favorite fish stall, he draped his arm over Caroline's shoulder, the possessive intimacy of the gesture making her stiffen up even more.

"Do you want to walk around a bit?" he asked.

Caroline quickly concurred—anything to postpone reaching his cabin. They spent nearly an hour browsing through the multilevel, two-block-long market, which contained over a hundred stalls and shops selling jewelry, clothing, and antiques, craft items, food, and furniture. Matthew picked up several bottles of wine and an assortment of fresh baked goods and waited patiently while Caroline window-shopped at one of the

leather goods stores. Together they selected fresh produce and fish, and as they were leaving Matthew
bought a bouquet of flowers and handed it to her.
Caroline was pleased by his thoughtfulness, but had to
wonder if he purchased fresh flowers for all his weekend companions.

She knew that her nervousness must be obvious, but
Matthew made no comment on it, either while they
wandered through the market or afterward, as they
packed the additional groceries into the car. He seemed
to be in no hurry to reach Anacortes, because he
quickly abandoned the most direct route in favor of a
more scenic one. Caroline was relieved when he cut
west to Mukilteo, the terminal for yet another one of
the state's ferries. This one connected the mainland
with Whidbey Island, and they arrived just in time to
drive onto the waiting boat.

"Would you like a cup of coffee?" They were the first
words Matthew had directed to Caroline since they had
left Seattle. Only the pop music coming from the car
radio had eased the silence. She quickly said that she
would, unsettled by the prospect of sitting alone in the
car with him in the dim depths of the large ferry.

Since the trip took only twenty minutes, they had just
enough time to buy their coffee in the ferry's cafeteria
and sit down at a table to drink it. Caroline occupied
herself by looking out the window, watching Whidbey
Island loom closer and closer.

Whidbey Island was fifty miles long and narrow
enough that Puget Sound was usually visible from the
two-lane road that traversed it vertically. It was one of
the largest islands in the United States, the climate a
little milder than in Seattle, spring in fuller bloom.
Cattle and horses, sometimes accompanied by frolick-

ing newborns, grazed in the pastures abutting the road. The clouds were drifting eastward, and frequently the sun broke through to add warmth and sparkle to the fresh, early April day. Occasional sailboats skimmed across the water, their sails billowing in the breeze.

Caroline found herself unwinding. Matthew was driving so slowly that it would be evening by the time they reached the San Juans. There was no point in becoming hysterical just yet. She had skipped breakfast, too keyed up to eat, and was just about to ask about lunch when Matthew turned off the main road at Deception Pass State Park. He parked the car near a picnic area.

"Why don't you sit down over there, Carrie, and I'll get the food," he invited pointing to a shaded redwood picnic table with two benches.

He carried over the cracked crab and sourdough French bread they had purchased earlier, and Caroline attacked the food with relish. She also shared the small bottle of chilled white wine that he uncorked.

They ate and drank in silence, Caroline finding pleasure in the lovely, quiet cove only yards away and in the feel of the gentle breeze on her skin. When Matthew suggested a short walk along a nearby trail, she readily agreed. There were several other picnickers in the park, and she felt relatively safe.

"Have you had any lovers since Clay died?"

The soft question, totally unexpected after hours of near silence, so flustered Caroline that she almost stumbled. He had no right to such personal information. She had made that quite clear only yesterday afternoon. She refused to answer him, simply kept on walking.

"Answer me, Carrie. I want to know."

"Why?" she flared, confused and angered by his persistence. "It's none of your business, just like my marriage."

"Yes, it is my business," he said. "It's completely different from your marriage, because it has an effect on what happens tonight. I didn't miss your reaction the first time I kissed you. You were shocked. It threw me." He was absent mindedly kicking a stone as he walked along, his head down. "Until today, though, I still assumed that I had had a fair number of predecessors. Now I'm not so sure. You're so nervous, I have to wonder if I'm the first since your husband died."

When Caroline made no reply, he stopped her by putting a hand on her shoulder. She shuddered involuntarily.

"You *are* nervous, aren't you!"

"All right, yes! I don't do this sort of thing all the time. Unlike you," she added sourly, glaring at him.

"What gives you the idea that my life is full of women?" Matthew asked, his mouth twitching with amusement.

"Isn't it?"

By now he was grinning down at her. "Of course not. I don't usually have the time to take four-day weekends. This is a special occasion, Carrie. Now stop spitting at me and tell me if there's been anyone since Clay."

Although glad to learn that she wasn't the latest in a succession of weekend conquests, Caroline still rebelled at Matthew's prying attitude. Unfortunately, he was obviously going to keep demanding an answer until she supplied one, so she gave in. "No. No one," she murmured.

His hand dropped from her shoulder to his side and he gave the stone another kick. It skittered ahead and

Matthew followed, his eyebrows knitted together thoughtfully.

Caroline hoped that he would be sensitive enough to drop the subject of her personal life. But only a minute later he stopped her again and said, "You jump every time I come close to you. I have to ask myself why, since you always let me overcome your objections in the end. It occurs to me that Clay Spencer was old enough to be your grandfather. Did you enjoy it when he made love to you?"

Caroline felt herself whiten. Every time she had contemplated the weekend ahead, the same question had tormented her. Should she tell Matthew that he was going to be her first lover? If she did, there was bound to be an inquisition. He would insist on knowing every detail of her marriage, and her nervousness would make her vulnerable enough to tell him. How could she share such experiences with someone she didn't love and trust?

It would be different if Matthew found out while he was making love to her. She would be able to handle him once it was all over with. Her defenses would be intact, her fear only a memory. She would be able to tell him that it was none of his business and make it stick.

Now she decided that since Clay Spencer had never even touched her, she could hardly have enjoyed making love with him. And if her answer was misleading, so be it. "No," she replied.

She waited tensely for him to hound her with follow-up questions: Why did you marry him? What did he do to you? Why did you stay with him?

Matthew's hand was still on her shoulder. She stared at his chest. His sweat shirt read LELAND STANFORD JUNIOR UNIVERSITY—ORGANIZED 1891. She could feel his eyes studying her. He took a step closer, one hand sliding around her back, the fingers of the other lifting her chin. Caroline looked into his eyes, seeking to read his expression, but saw only enigmatic blankness. What was he thinking? Did he know that her heart was pounding out of control? Had he noticed the way her body had just quivered at his touch?

When his lips brushed hers, she went rigid, unable to cope with the feelings rushing through her body. She didn't want to respond to him. She had all but decided to walk out on him once they reached the San Juans, but when he touched her this way her common sense evaporated. She kept staring straight ahead while he played with her mouth, but when he eased his head away and forced her to look at him, his gaze was so passionately intense that her lids flickered down, her eyes unable to hold that hungry stare.

He lowered his head once again, his lips slightly parted, caressing first her upper lip, then her lower one, the tip of his tongue probing the crevice between the two. The feel of his mouth made her feverish with longing, and she was terrified at how easily he could make her hover on the brink of insane abandonment. She tried to turn her head, but his fingers, which had been stroking her face, tightened into a firm grip to hold her mouth under his own.

"Carrie," he mumbled against her lips. "It's driving me crazy—what you're doing . . ." His voice was hoarse, rough.

But she wasn't doing anything, was she? His mouth hardened, his tongue demanding entry, no longer gentle against her lips. His breathless arousal intensified her own to the point that she could no longer passively resist him. Part of her wanted to run away, but Matthew was holding her captive, preventing any escape. And the part of her that was content to be a prisoner triumphed.

She lifted her arms and coiled them around his neck. Her body arched invitingly. Her lips parted to welcome his kiss, an urgent probing that made her feel as though his mouth was literally scorching her own. As his tongue moved against hers, exploring her mouth hungrily, everything else in the world seemed to fade. Clinging to him like this, she was only too aware of how much he wanted her. And the low, deep moans coming from her own throat told her she had been captured by the same wild feelings.

Matthew broke the embrace. "I can't take any more of this," he muttered. He took her hand and dragged her back to the picnic table. There was still some wine left in the bottle, and he swallowed it quickly, not bothering with the plastic cup. "It won't be the way it was with Clay," he said brusquely. "Do you believe that now?"

Caroline was still shaking from what they had just shared. "Is that why you did that? To prove a point?" she asked in a low voice.

"That's how it started. But when you stand there like that, not moving, I can't take it. Because I can feel you wanting me and resisting it. I can't stop myself from forcing you to respond when I'd rather not have to do that, Carrie. It's criminal that you were married to Spencer for over four years and wasted all that sensuality."

She had nothing to say to such a startling observation. She had never considered herself sensual. How could she, when her body had never once hinted to her that it could be capable of the deep passion Matthew had so easily aroused? There was no longer any question of what would happen tonight. He would take her in his arms and she would lose all control over her actions. Perhaps she would be afraid at first and stiffen up when his hands caressed her body. It wouldn't stop Matthew. On the contrary, he had just admitted that it would only make him more determined to break down her defenses. He would touch her and kiss her until she begged him to take anything he wanted.

As she sat silently brooding about the mess she had landed herself in, Matthew gathered up the trash and deposited it into a convenient can. The conversation was apparently at an end, at least for the moment, and Caroline was grateful for that small mercy. They walked back to the car and started north again, traveling over the spectacular bridge that spanned Deception Pass, the narrow channel of water separating Whidbey Island from Fidalgo Island. The town of Anacortes was at the northwest tip of the latter.

Caroline's agitation increased as they neared their destination. Caroline Spencer, the Mata Hari of Seattle—it was laughable. She was emotionally involved with Matthew Lyle right to the top of her blonde head, and that was a considerable distance. By the time this weekend was over, he would possess not only her body, which perhaps she could accept, but her soul as well. He would teach her to crave his lovemaking, to fling herself into his arms whenever he decided he could spare a few hours from his busy schedule. And there would be nothing she could do about it.

At the moment, he might burn to make love to her, but how would he feel once the weekend was over and he had assuaged both his curiosity and his lust? Would he be cool and impersonal, just another board member at her quarterly meetings? The thought of it tore her apart.

She had to get away from him, but unfortunately, if

she was sure of anything, she was sure that Matthew Lyle had no intention of letting her escape. If she aroused his suspicions, he would guard her like some dangerous felon. Once they were on the ferry, perhaps she could excuse herself to go to the ladies' room and talk some sympathetic woman into hiding her on her camper. Then again, Matthew would probably wait at the door until she emerged.

That meant she would have to steal away from the cabin itself. Caroline panicked at the realization that, her earlier assumptions aside, the house might be in some isolated spot, miles from anything else. She had to find out whether she could even afford to wait until they reached the San Juans before attempting her escape. It took her several minutes to settle herself down enough to affect the proper casual air.

"Matthew," she asked, "just where *is* your cabin?"

He paused, just for a moment, then answered, "On Orcas Island, near Deer Harbor."

Caroline leaned back against the seat, so relieved that she felt drained of emotion. He had named one of the most developed spots on Orcas, which in turn was the most built up of the San Juan group. Thank heavens Matthew Lyle had a taste for luxury!

As she stared out the window, watching the scenery, she spotted the turnoff to the ferry. Matthew ignored it, whizzing right past the access road.

"You missed the turn," she blurted out.

"There's no ferry this time of day, Carrie. It leaves in the morning." Matthew's tone was conversational, but Caroline didn't miss the amused undercurrent. Where was he taking her?

She soon had her answer. There was a marina a few miles down the road, and as Matthew made a right turn toward the water, he pointed toward the dozens of boats lined up by the pier. "I keep one of my boats down there. It's a nice little cabin cruiser. In fact, if you don't like the cabin, we could sleep on board the boat."

His "nice little cabin cruiser" turned out to be a 42-foot customized yacht with a 14-foot mahogany-paneled salon, a fully equipped galley complete with microwave oven, and two carpeted staterooms with private heads. Caroline, following him back to the pier after a tour of the boat, looked dubiously at the waters of Rosario Strait. The wind was picking up, making the craft sway back and forth in the water. Caroline's stomach swayed along with the yacht.

"Matthew," she said, "I'm not a very good sailor. Couldn't we wait for the morning ferry?" By Saturday morning, she added silently, I'll be long gone.

"No problem," he replied cheerfully, taking her hand. "Come with me." He led her back through to the master stateroom, with its mirrored closets and queen-sized bedroom suite, and into the adjoining head. A quick perusal of the medicine cabinet produced a bottle of seasickness pills.

"Take one of these. I'll bring everything on board. You can wait on the pier if you'll be more comfortable."

Caroline poured herself a paper cup full of water and swallowed the yellow pill. Motion sickness medicine always made her sleepy, which was unfortunate, because she would need a clear head when the boat docked. But the alternative was even worse; repeated bouts of nausea were hardly conducive to romance *or* an easy escape.

She watched from the dock as Matthew carried the suitcases and supplies on board the boat. Later she found that he had stowed the perishables in the galley refrigerator and everything else in the built-in storage cabinets of the salon. With the politeness she had come to expect, he helped her back on board, then suggested that she sit up on the bridge with him. "Just keep your eyes on the horizon. The pill should take effect in another fifteen minutes or so."

The breeze against Caroline's face helped dispel her queasiness, if not her tension. Matthew was taking his time, the boat cruising at about 10 knots even though she could easily make double that speed.

Before, as Caroline stood on the pier, she had noticed the name *Desirée* painted on the side of the boat in italic letters, right next to the words *Lyle Marine* and the model number. In spite of her nervousness, she felt a certain curiosity about the owner of that exotic name, and couldn't resist asking Matthew who the lady was.

"Did you think she'd be a Vegas show girl?" he asked with a grin. "My grandfather was French Canadian, and Desirée is my mother's name. Dad's retired now, so they live in Palm Springs for most of the year."

So much for her speculation about fondly remembered former mistresses. Caroline leaned back in her padded armchair, suddenly sleepy. The motion of the boat was no longer uncomfortable, it was soporific. Wine and the medication made a potent combination, and Caroline didn't bother to fight it. She dozed off, waking up only when Matthew gently shook her shoulder.

"Go downstairs and lie down," he urged. "We won't be there for a few hours."

Caroline was only too content to take his advice. At least if she fell asleep again she wouldn't be able to torture herself with endlessly rehearsed scenarios of future escape attempts. The boat must have an automatic pilot, and she didn't want to issue invitations, so she prudently avoided the master stateroom. Instead, she curled up in one of the twin beds in the guest room.

It seemed only minutes later that her eyelids reluctantly opened, fluttered down again, and reopened. She yawned, stretched, and glanced at her watch, amazed to find that she had slept for almost an hour and a half. She swayed dizzily when she got off the bed and sat down at a vanity to tidy her hair back into its usual prim bun.

When she wandered back into the salon, she found Matthew sitting at the lower helm station. Since he was not piloting the boat, she inferred that the craft was indeed on automatic.

He smiled at her as soon as he noticed her standing in the entryway. "Time for something to eat, I think. Sleep well?"

"Yes. Is it much farther, Matthew?" Caroline asked softly, her face solemn. They had been traveling for about two hours already.

"I'll show you in a minute. Sit down on the couch, Carrie." Since her legs were still rubbery, she was happy to comply.

The cushions were soft and comfortable—the nubby tweed sofa could have graced the most expensive of dens. Matthew disappeared into the galley, emerging a few minutes later carrying a clear plastic tray holding a bottle of imported champagne, two glasses, a bowl of crackers, and an assortment of tinned pâtés. Caroline thought nervously that the man was probably well practiced in organizing seductions.

"First have a glass of champagne and something to eat. Then we'll go back up to the bridge and I'll point out my cabin as soon as it comes into view."

He set the tray on an oak coffee table, uncorked the

wine, and poured out a glass for each of them. Caroline picked up her own and sipped, barely appreciating the dry, biting taste. She knew that it was unwise to drink any more alcohol, but she needed something to calm her down.

Ever since she had woken from her nap, Matthew's whole manner had disturbed her. On the surface he was perfectly polite, even attentive. But underneath she had the disquieting suspicion that he was laughing at her, and she didn't understand why.

She accepted several crackers spread with assorted pâtés, all of them delicious, and finished the generous glassful of champagne that Matthew had poured for her. He lazed back on the couch, his booted feet sprawled out on the coffee table, and ate with unhurried enjoyment. Neither of them spoke.

Numerous tree-covered islands passed in and out of view as Caroline stared through the salon windows. Those closest to the boat were verdant with Douglas fir and madrone; the more distant islands appeared only as bluish smears in the afternoon haze.

Matthew swung his feet from the table, stood, and held out his hand to Caroline. "You wanted to see my cabin, right, sweetheart?"

The endearment, drawled so lazily, made her want to jump up and run outside. Instead she rose gracefully and proudly, ignored his hand, and marched from the salon. Whatever his wretched game was, she wouldn't let him intimidate her!

Out on the bridge, Matthew hooked an arm over her shoulder and pointed to their right. "That's Lummi Island over there, and to the left is the northern shore of Orcas. Deer Harbor is on the *south* shore of Orcas. If we were going to Deer Harbor, we would have headed west from Anacortes. We didn't go west. We went north. My island is straight ahead."

Caroline's voice was a strangled yelp. "Your *what?*"

"Carrie," he admonished with a broad grin, "if I had told you that I was taking you to a private island up near Sucia Island, you probably would have locked yourself into the ladies' room on the Whidbey ferry and refused to come out. So I didn't tell you."

"You—you lied to me!" she cried, jerking away from his arm. Good grief, was he really taking her to a secluded *private island?* What on earth was she going to do?

"Of course I did," he replied equably. "Why should I let your last-minute attack of nerves ruin my weekend?" He smiled crookedly down at her. "By Sunday night you'll thank me for kidnapping you; I promise you that, Carrie."

Caroline was too distraught to think of objecting to such egotistical overconfidence. She sat down in the captain's chair, suddenly dizzy again, and murmured, "Please, take me back, Matthew. I've changed my mind. You wouldn't enjoy it, with me fighting you."

"You won't fight me. We've been through all that already, Carrie."

Both of them knew he was right. Caroline couldn't claim otherwise. "Then—then later," she stammered. "Afterward—Matthew, I . . ."

"Afterward I'll make love to you again," he interrupted. "Get it through your head that I have no intention of turning back. And that both of us are going to enjoy every one of the next forty-eight hours. I want you, and nothing is going to stop me from taking you."

Matthew's impatience alarmed her. A man didn't succeed in business as he had without a certain ruthless streak in him, as his last words confirmed. He took what he wanted. Caroline didn't want to find herself on the wrong end of his temper. So far he had simply toyed with her, pressuring but not really forcing her, confident of her eventual cooperation. And why not? Every time he touched her, fire swamped all thoughts of icy resistence or angry rebellion. He couldn't understand what she was afraid of. As long as everything went well in bed, it would be a terrific weekend for him. But not for her.

"What happens Sunday night?" she asked, her voice almost a whisper.

He chose to misinterpret the question. "The same thing as tonight, tomorrow, and tomorrow night. I'll make love to you. We're not leaving until Monday morning."

"Monday night, then. When we're back in Seattle." Caroline couldn't look at him. His anger was all too apparent in the tautness of his body and the coldness of his eyes.

"Women!" was the long-suffering retort. "I'm not allowed to ask you questions, but you want all kinds of commitments. You and I have a business arrangement, Carrie. I signed on for a weekend in bed with you, period. How on earth should I know what's going to happen? I'm not a bloody clairvoyant!" He grabbed her arm. "Out of my seat. I have to pilot the boat the rest of the way."

Caroline moved to the other chair as he switched the yacht back to manual and increased speed. Too distressed to think clearly, she began to fidget with the ties on her windbreaker, convulsively twining them around first one finger, then another.

"For heaven's sake, Carrie, I'm not going to jump

you the minute we get in the door. I'm not totally insensitive," Matthew snapped. "I understand that you're nervous. We've been through all *that,* too!"

Nervous? She felt as if the world was crashing down on her.

"We'll have dinner first," he continued more patiently. "We'll enjoy the fire, relax over Irish coffee. You act like a cornered virgin in the clutches of some invading barbarian warrior. I've told you, it won't be like it was with Clay. I'll make sure of that."

A cornered virgin? Caroline leaned back in her chair and closed her eyes, fighting down the urge to giggle. That's exactly what she was. But by tomorrow morning only one of those words would apply. Matthew would take her innocence, persuasively, passionately, gently, and expertly, and afterward she would be even more trapped than she was now.

Chapter Six

Caroline couldn't continue to sit motionless up on the bridge next to Matthew Lyle when every instinct told her to keep arguing for her freedom. Pleading with him would accomplish nothing but her own humiliation, and having suffered more than enough of *that* at his hands, she flung herself out of her seat and hurried back to the salon. As she climbed down the ladder she found herself contemplating the waters below. She wasn't a strong enough swimmer to jump over the side and make it to the nearest island. Even if she tried it, Matthew would only haul her out.

She sat down on the couch and tried to calm herself; the half-empty magnum of champagne caught her attention. She poured a glass and tasted it. Why hadn't she noticed how superb this wine was—tart and dry, absolutely perfect! She finished up the glassful and poured another, then finished it quickly. The boat was rolling quite independently of the choppy seas by now, and Caroline giggled at the idea that if she drank enough, she might even pass out. Matthew would be furious! Somehow the thought merely amused, rather than terrified, her.

She was on her third glass when the boat slowed and had finished it by the time it stopped. She tried to focus her eyes on the scene outside the window. She saw no cabin—only a strip of sand littered with gray driftwood and a dirt path that disappeared into the woods.

Matthew's sudden appearance failed to disturb her. He glanced at the almost-empty bottle and began to laugh. "If you think I'm going to object to making love to you when you're tipsy, you're wrong, Carrie," he drawled. "It might even be entertaining."

"I don't see any cabin," she said, oblivious to his comment. Why had she been so agitated before? It was quite lovely up here, and anyway, it was hours until bedtime.

Matthew walked over, took both of her hands, and pulled her up. "Come with me. You look like you could use some help."

Caroline *did* feel exceedingly wobbly, but disguised that fact fairly well as she tottered out onto the pier and followed Matthew into the woods. The path was covered with evergreen needles and felt spongy underneath her feet. It had sprinkled here recently and everything smelled fresh and earthy.

When the cabin came into view, she frowned. It was so tiny, the rough Douglas fir exterior so uncivilized-looking. Matthew unlocked the door and she stepped inside. There was only one room, with the stone fireplace at the back wall, ancient hooked rugs on the planked wood floor, and a sink in an el at the left. Caroline saw no faucets—only a pump. A single couch was set some distance from the fireplace; several lanterns and a Coleman stove rested on a table near the sink.

"*This* is where we're going to stay?" she asked in confusion. "There's no bedroom." She wondered why Matthew had started to laugh again.

"The couch unfolds into a double bed," he informed her. "But if the setup is too primitive for you, we could always retire to the boat." He sat Caroline down on the couch, mumbling something about black coffee, then picked up some newspaper and kindling that were stacked near the fireplace and started a fire.

The damp, cold interior of the cabin was soon cozy and warm. Matthew added several large logs to the fire and announced that he would be down at the boat for a while. As the door closed, Caroline mused that she had never pictured the man in such surroundings. But of course—cabins didn't interest him! Only boats, companies, and women, she thought with a giggle. Her brain jumped to a related thought. There was something very raw and wild about this environment. It conjured up images of seduction and ravishment. Matthew would be wonderful at seduction and ravishment, Caroline thought with a sigh, then caught herself and blushed.

It was quite some time before Matthew reappeared with their suitcases, only to return to the boat immediately to fetch the supplies they would need that night. "This is for you, Carrie," he said, unscrewing a thermos and pouring some coffee into the plastic cover.

She silently accepted it. The initial effects of the champagne were wearing off now, and she felt a little queasy. The situation no longer seemed hugely amusing.

Matthew lit two of the lanterns and began to prime

the propane stove, whistling to himself. "Hey, Carrie," he called to her, "are you sober enough to fix a salad?"

She nodded mutely. Why had she had so much to drink? She poured out another cup of coffee and carried it over to the counter. Matthew was rummaging through a drawer holding utensils and flatware and finally dug out a knife and peeler for her. A wooden chopping block sat on the counter next to the sink. "Be careful with the knife," he said. "I want to make love to you later, not run you to the nearest emergency room."

Make love. Why did he use that phrase when love had nothing to do with what would happen later tonight? Caroline tried to focus on peeling and cutting, and in her present state those tasks took her full concentration. The aroma of salmon sautéing in butter would normally have piqued her appetite, but everything was fading into unreality. She was intelligent enough to understand what was happening to her. Her emotions had seesawed too crazily all day, and her brain was refusing to process any more apprehension, arousal, or amusement.

Her defenses had automatically taken over, just as they had so often done with Clay. Some other woman was tossing the salad, sitting down at the small, round table with Matthew, eating his food and refusing his wine. Part of her was making light conversation about this island and finding it fascinating that Matthew and his father had built the cabin themselves, while the rest of her was looking on, totally disconnected from Matthew Lyle and Caroline Spencer.

After they washed the dishes, some other woman heard him say matter-of-factly, "You can use the head in the boat to change. I'll walk you down there. I have to put a few things back into the refrigerator."

Caroline nodded, removed her toothbrush, cosmetic case, and nightgown from the suitcase, and never even noticed Matthew's laughter at the last item. It was almost dark as they walked to the boat, so he took along an electric lantern to light the path.

It was only as Caroline stared at herself in the mirror that she began to snap out of her dazed state. She realized that all thought of resistance had been drained out of her. At the moment, she wanted only to get this over with.

She loosened her hair and picked up her toothbrush. As soon as she put it into her mouth, a wave of nausea hit her. Why did the blasted boat have to sway this way? It made her feel dreadful. She had just managed to finish washing her face and was absentmindedly brushing her hair again when she heard two sharp raps on the door. "You've been in there for twenty minutes, Carrie. You can't keep me waiting like this and expect me to take it slow when you finally come out."

When she made no reply, Matthew opened the door, his eyes blazing into hers when they met in the mirror. Caroline looked down at the sink. Her adrenaline was pumping again. Why did her mind insist that she keep resisting him?

His hands settled onto her waist, unerringly moving upward to caress the curves hidden beneath the loose nightgown. "Enough is enough, Carrie. I'm tired of playing Boy Scout." He bent his head to her neck, his lips nuzzling aside her platinum hair to kiss the skin underneath.

Caroline felt feverish and dizzy, but her symptoms owed nothing to arousal. She was leaning back against Matthew, but only because she felt she would faint if she didn't. He seemed oblivious to her misery. His hands were roaming over her body as he whispered something about how beautiful she was.

The boat lurched; Caroline's stomach protested violently. The next instant she tore herself out of his arms and leaned over the sink, where she was repeatedly and wretchedly sick. Tears were streaming down her face. It was the first time she had cried in years—ever since she had sworn for the twentieth time that Clay Spencer's tirades would no longer have the power to affect her and had finally made it stick.

It was several minutes before she was able to take some fresh water and straighten up. She clutched at a guest towel and dried her eyes, avoiding her own tear-streaked face in the mirror. She couldn't look at Matthew, either. In twenty-four years she had never made such a display of herself.

"It's all right, sweetheart," he said soothingly, turning her around to face him. "Next time I'll hide the champagne. Come sit over here." He carried her into the master stateroom, laid her down, and returned a moment later with a cold, damp washcloth and another glass of water.

Caroline closed her eyes and let him gently sponge off her face. She managed to sip a little of the water as well. Now that her stomach was empty she felt much better, although she was still woozy and her head had begun to throb. Matthew swept her into his arms again and carried her back to the cabin, and she rested her head against his shoulder, relieved that she wouldn't have to walk.

When he set her down on one of the dinette chairs, she shivered, suddenly chilled. Matthew quickly flipped the cushions off the couch and pulled out the convertible bed, then fetched pillows, sheets, and blankets and made it up. Caroline had no time to wonder just what he had in mind before he took her from the chair and deposited her between the sheets.

"Matthew," she said in a low voice as he sat down beside her, "I really don't think—I mean—I don't feel too well, and . . ."

"You can't be serious!" He looked heavenward in exasperation. "I know you're in no shape for anything but sleep. One more night of membership in the Boy Scouts won't kill me."

Caroline was only aware of her tension when she felt it begin to drain away. "Is it really such a relief?" Matthew smiled.

Caroline didn't need to answer. Her reddening face was all the response he needed. "Okay. I won't tease you. How do you feel?"

"Woozy. My head is throbbing."

"Do you think you can manage a glass of water and some aspirin?"

When she nodded, he poured the water from a plastic jug and fished the aspirin out of his suitcase. Caroline obediently swallowed the pills, her right hand going automatically to her head once she handed Matthew the empty glass.

"Let me. Show me where it hurts." He stretched out next to her and cradled her head on his chest, his fingers kneading her temples and the back of her neck, loosening the taut muscles, making her want to purr. She snuggled against him, grateful that the pain was easing.

"Better?"

"Umm."

"Your hair's all tangled. I'll brush it for you," he murmured.

Caroline smiled dreamily. "A closet hairdresser?"

"Depends who's in the closet with me." It took him

only a moment to locate her brush among the cosmetics in her case.

"Lean back," he said, propping her up against several pillows and sitting beside her. When he had positioned her head to his satisfaction, he began to brush her hair with sensuous, soothing strokes.

Caroline closed her eyes, utterly content. "How much do you usually drink?" he asked softly, his voice full of amusement.

"A glass or two of wine."

"You must have killed nearly a fifth between the picnic and the champagne. No wonder you got sick," he scolded. His fingers brushed against her chin, turning her head so he could reach the other side.

At some point, he tossed the brush onto the bed and helped Caroline snuggle down between the covers. His lips covered hers in an undemanding kiss, but she was too sleepy to respond. The last thing she remembered was the feel of his fingers, lazily rubbing her back.

She woke to the smell of frying bacon, bolted upright, and stared at Matthew. Memories of the previous evening came flooding back, causing her to pull the covers up to her chin. A glance at the rumpled pillowcase next to her left little doubt about where he had slept.

"Good morning," he said. "How about some bacon and eggs?"

Caroline was surprised at how hungry she was, and she desperately wanted something cold to drink. "I'm so thirsty," she croaked.

"The penalty for overindulgence," he teased, pouring a glass of juice and bringing it over to her.

Her body snapped to attention the minute he sat

down on the bed next to her. "I thought you were over all that," Matthew said, a long-suffering look on his face. "Listen to me, Carrie. I may be tough when it comes to business, but I don't treat women like business adversaries. I want to relax and enjoy myself up here. You've got to stop pinning negative labels on me."

If anything Caroline thought, he deserved exactly the opposite. He had been as tender and caring as any woman could wish for last night. She sipped the juice, avoiding his eyes. "I don't," she murmured. "You were very sweet to me, Matthew."

He reached out a hand to stroke her hair. "I can be a lot sweeter. We still have two days, Carrie."

Caroline had no response to that. Her emotions were in turmoil. She had never met anybody like Matthew Lyle in her life, and she realized that she was captivated by him. Alternately tough and tender, passionate and sweet, teasing and angry, he had undermined her determination to hold herself aloof from all personal involvements. He was frank about his desire for her and equally blunt in refusing to commit himself. He made no secret of the fact that her unwillingness to talk about Clay irritated him, and yet he could be patient with her beyond all her expectations. She was falling in love with him in spite of her reluctance to let herself care for anyone ever again.

"Carrie?"

"I can't go through with this, Matthew," she burst out. "It's all wrong. I never should have agreed . . ."

"Why? What are you so frightened of? What did Clay Spencer do to you to make you fight off every other man in the world?"

Caroline's hands flew to her ears. "Clay, Clay, Clay!!

You're always going on about Clay!" The objection was wrenched from her. "Why don't we ever talk about you?!"

"You want to know about me? Fine! I'll tell you about me!" He started stalking back and forth in the small room. "I had a perfect childhood. I have a younger sister named Terry who's married to a doctor. She writes children's stories. They live in Maine. I grew up in Seattle, attended Stanford as an undergrad, and decided to go on for a doctorate in economics. I was too bored to write the thesis. I came back up here and took over my father's company instead." Each sentence was flung out staccato style as he paced around. "I found I enjoyed it. When I acquired my first company, I enjoyed that even more. Especially when they fought me. Result: fourteen companies in ten years, not including your own."

He stopped and glared at her. "Women? Naturally you want to know about *that!* I'm thirty-five years old. I've had as many women as most men my age, which is somewhat fewer than the newspapers claim. I've probably been too wrapped up in my business to fall in love with any of them. Until I met you, I'd never lost my temper with a single one of them. I happen to *like* women; I like sleeping with them, and I think my relationships have been relatively unneurotic—" he paused a second or two—"until *now!* Your turn, Carrie!"

Neurotic? How dare he call her neurotic! He was the one who was crazy, with his blasted game of cat and mouse! "Just because I don't want to sleep with you that doesn't make me . . ."

"You *do* want to sleep with me," Matthew cut in. "And from what I can gather, I'm just about the first man to merit that great honor. You've frozen off every other guy who's tried to get close to you. So we come back to Clay Spencer."

A part of Caroline wanted to confide in him, but she simply couldn't risk it—not when he had all but told her that his obsession with his business precluded any long-term commitments. "I don't want to discuss it," she said.

He shook his head angrily and stormed off to the stove, swearing succinctly and curtly. "I'll make you some breakfast. Maybe it'll improve your mood," he tossed back at her.

In spite of the tension between them, Caroline managed to eat three slices of bacon, an omelet, and an English muffin. Matthew retired to the bed and lay back against the pillows, reading her feminist novel and frowning. Caroline didn't know what to do when she finished eating, so she stayed at the table and stared at the wall.

A startled shudder snaked through her body when Matthew tossed aside the book, which landed on the floor with a thud. "Come to bed, Carrie," he ordered softly.

She stood up abruptly, her arms crossed defensively in front of her chest. "I don't want to," she said. When he started to pull himself up, she added hurriedly, "I know you'll make me enjoy it, but I'll hate myself when it's over with. I can't sleep with a man I don't love—who doesn't love me."

"You slept with Clay Spencer," he reminded her sarcastically. "Don't try to tell me that you loved *him!*"

"I didn't!" Caroline had blurted out the words without thinking, replying to his first comment. But Matthew assumed they were a response to his second.

113

"Then why did you marry him?" he demanded furiously.

"I've told you, I won't discuss my marriage with you," Caroline answered. She was too upset to be angry anymore. She felt as though Matthew was hammering at her, always coming back to that same question. He had no right to do that. Why wouldn't he leave her alone?

"Great! Terrific! Don't then!" He was off the bed before she could move, picking her up and flinging her onto the mattress. She had no time to get up—he was on top of her at almost the same instant, his mouth forcing hers apart in a brutal, enraged kiss.

Caroline was too stunned to fight him off. Matthew had toyed with her, yelled at her, and teased her, but never, never had he hurt her. Tears filled her eyes and rolled down her cheeks, accomplishing what resistance would not have. Matthew released her, rolled away, and growled, "Damn it, don't start that! I've never wanted anyone the way I want you, and the last twenty-four hours have driven me just about insane. Do you have any idea how many times I've pulled back?"

He sighed, and went on more gently, "I don't want to hurt you, Carrie, but I just can't take any more of this."

Caroline couldn't take any more either. She was so tired of fighting both him and herself that her little remaining spirit flared briefly, then died. She lay on her back, no longer crying, simply exhausted and empty. Let him take what he wanted. She supposed she would even enjoy it. Time enough for tears when it was over.

"Please take it slowly, Matthew," she said, her tone flat. "It's the first time I've ever done this."

"I know that, Carrie." His voice was soft, tender. "I told you . . ."

"You don't understand," she broke in. "I said, *'the first time.'*"

From the look on Matthew's face, he would have been considerably less flabbergasted had she told him that she did this every weekend. "Are you trying to tell me that you never slept with your husband?" he asked incredulously.

"He . . . couldn't. I knew that when I married him." She was aware that Matthew might put the worst possible interpretation on that, but she didn't care anymore. It didn't matter.

"There are other ways of making love, Carrie."

She shook her head wearily. "He never touched me. He was dying of cancer when I married him."

"Dying of cancer," he repeated in a stunned tone of voice. "You knew he was dying when you married him?"

"That's right."

"How long . . . ?"

"A year, eighteen months at the most."

"And he lived four and a half."

"Yes."

"And left you everything when he died."

The statement required no confirmation. Caroline looked away from the harsh disapproval in Matthew's eyes. It stung her, bitterly. "I tried to make him happy," she said in a defeated little voice.

"Make him happy?" The words exploded down on her head. "When you wouldn't let the poor guy near you? He must have been absolutely besotted with you, to marry you on those terms. His life must have been one long frustrated agony. And I thought *he* had hurt *you!* Just what kind of sadistic, manipulative woman are you?"

It was the only reaction Caroline had expected, and it

would be impossible for her to correct it without a recitation of her entire life story. There was no reason for Matthew Lyle to sit and listen to it or believe her words were anything but self-serving if he did. After all, her reputation—icy, unapproachable Mount Carrie—had preceded her. It cut her like a lash to realize that his tenderness and caring of the night before had had only one motive: seduction in the morning.

When she continued to avoid his eyes, he stalked out of the cabin. Caroline took the opportunity to hastily pull on her clothing. When he returned, he was carrying the bottle of motion sickness pills.

During the endless, silent trip back to Seattle, Caroline considered Matthew's stinging condemnation. Had she been wrong to marry Clay without offering whatever physical relationship they might have shared together? He had desired her when he first proposed, but had given no sign that he continued to do so after his illness. And hadn't one of his doctors taken her aside after their marriage and tactfully explained that the combination of surgery and medication would render Clay incapable of making theirs a normal marriage? No, she had no reason to reproach herself.

Even during those last few painful years with Clay, she had never felt so raw, so hurt. She seemed to bring out the volatile side of Matthew's nature, but when he had lost his temper in the past, he had always apologized. He apparently had no intention of doing so now. On the contrary, it seemed that he couldn't wait to be rid of her. He was stiff and withdrawn, cruising the boat at top speed to Anacortes and taking the shortest route south in the car.

His innate courtesy, which had previously been so

appealing to Caroline, became an agony. He helped her onto the boat and off again, his fingers firm under her arm. At her house he took her suitcase out of the trunk for her and carried it down the drive, all without saying a word. Caroline risked an upward glance when they reached the door, but dropped her eyes in the face of the angry condemnation she saw in his. She rummaged clumsily in her purse for her house key, but Matthew had already turned to leave. He was well up the drive by the time she unlocked the door.

Dejected, she carried the case downstairs to her bedroom to unpack it. She had removed every reminder of Clay Spencer from this house three months after his death, redecorated all the rooms, given away his clothing, thrown out personal mementos, but it had not exorcised the painful memories she had of him. The trauma inflicted by her four and a half year marriage remained.

If the years with Clay had scarred Caroline, they had also left her with a strength of purpose and a brisk self-confidence unusual in a woman her age. She was too sensible to lie in bed feeling sorry for herself and spent the rest of the day walking in the rain, baking bread, and watching television. These solitary pursuits failed to take her mind off Matthew.

By Sunday morning, she knew that she needed some violent physical exercise and undemanding company if her own thoughts weren't to drive her mad. Her weekly basketball games were held on Saturday mornings, but she had never had any problem picking up a game at other times of the week. She changed into a T-shirt and shorts and drove over to the gym.

Fortunately, there were only seven players on the court, and she was welcomed enthusiastically as the eighth. Two of the boys were on her regular team, and she had played against most of the others during the past few years. Their smiling acceptance was a relief. She soon felt like she was a teenager again, losing herself on the basketball court as she had always done.

After an hour and a half of playing four on four she was gratefully exhausted. The game had done wonders for her ego—her shooting had been dazzling—and the admiring looks of her fellow players certainly hadn't hurt either. One of the boys, an undergraduate named Joey whom she had met only once before, sat down next to her on the bleachers. He held out his soda for her to sip.

"You're really good," he said. "All the guys talk about you—especially Brad. I don't usually play weekends, but I came yesterday and today, hoping you'd be around."

"Thanks," Caroline replied easily. "Any special reason or do you just like to play against women?" It struck her that her own resilience was a wondrous thing. How delightful to be able to tease the boy so lightheartedly, when only this morning she had been engulfed in misery. She found it sweet that he blushed at her question and thought what a shame it was that these delightfully open young men would turn into arrogant brutes like Matthew Lyle someday.

"You play like a guy," Joey said quickly. "But there *is* a reason I wanted to speak to you. I have a little sister—she's in high school—and they've been talking about starting a girls' team. But there's no decent coach. Brad was over at the house last week for dinner, and Lindsay, my sister, heard him talking about you. She's been after me ever since to find out if you would coach her team."

118

Caroline smiled at him, naturally and warmly. "I already have a job, Joey, but thanks for the offer. I'm flattered."

"It would only be two nights a week," he coaxed. "It wouldn't interfere with EBE, Carrie."

Something about that last sentence nagged at her. It wasn't the reference to EBE. Most of the boys knew she was a corporate president and even needled her about it in a good-natured way. But Caroline was too interested in Joey's offer to dwell on it just then. "Your sister and her friends—are they any good?" she asked.

"Not bad, for girls," was the crushing evaluation. "At least you'd have some decent raw material to work with."

Once Caroline had planned to make a career of teaching sports and coaching, and the idea of working with an enthusiastic group of high school girls was appealing. "I think it would be fun. Tell your sister to call me, and we'll talk it over. I'm in the book, listed under C.M. Spencer on Mercer Island."

"Gee, thanks Carrie." Joey grinned. "I'm going to tell Lindsay that she owes me one."

And then Caroline realized what had bothered her before. No one here addressed her as Carrie. They called her Caroline, like almost everyone else. "What did you call me?" she demanded.

His face slowly turned scarlet. "Uh . . . yeah. I guess I picked that up from my parents. You're a hot topic of conversation around the dinner table."

"Why?" The question was frosty.

"I was going to tell you, Carrie. I wouldn't have . . ."

"Tell me *what*?" she interrupted.

119

"My name. It's Joseph Symington, Jr. Okay? Does it make a difference?"

Oh, no! Wasn't she ever going to escape Matthew Lyle's tentacles? Of all the people in the world, why did this boy have to be his cousin's son?

Joey apparently deduced from her silence that his identity presented a considerable problem. "Don't say no, Carrie," he pleaded. "My parents . . . I know they don't agree with Matt's tactics. But it's his company and no one can stop him from running it just the way he wants. Don't hold it against my sister."

Caroline sourly digested this piece of information. She remembered Joe Symington's unexpected look the day they had met—the sympathy on his face. "Really?" she drawled. "And what tactics would those be?"

Joey was virtually squirming with embarrassment on the narrow bleacher seat, but Caroline had no intention of sparing him. "Joey?" she prompted.

"I don't know," he said, nursing the can of soda to avoid her eyes. "I guess, when Matt wants a company, he usually doesn't goof around. I mean, he doesn't play games with press leaks or take his time about filing for a proxy fight. He just goes after it."

"Unlike EBE." Caroline's expression was thoughtful. "So why did he do it, Joey?" she asked, wondering just how much he really knew.

"Oh, come on, Carrie. I can't . . ."

"Joey?" Caroline drew out his name, her intimidating tone demanding a straight answer.

Joey Symington looked plaintively over at her. "Don't get mad, Carrie. Matt's a great guy. But you're just so beautiful. Maybe—maybe he's sort of—obsessed with *you* even more than he is with your

120

company." He groped for the proper comparison. "Like he was with Cascade Mining!"

"Have your sister call me," Caroline snapped in exasperation, and stalked out of the gym. To be compared to a mining company! It was the ultimate humiliation!

Chapter Seven

Caroline's fury blazed briefly, sputtered, and was quenched by her own honesty. Ever since that final, tempestuous argument with Matthew, she had been trying to convince herself that he was an insensitive, manipulative beast who had blithely trampled on her feelings. The only lesson to be learned from the whole fiasco was to avoid entanglements in the future—entanglements with any man, but especially with Matthew Lyle.

It was time to face reality. She was her own worst enemy. Matthew had made it clear that he wasn't a womanizer, that he disdained one-night stands, and that he wanted to know her better. She was trapped by her own wariness, afraid to trust him because he didn't love her, yet aware that it was unrealistic to expect love when she let him receive the worst possible impression of her.

Could she really have tumbled into love so rapidly? At the moment it felt that way, much to her distress. She didn't want to give Matthew the power to hurt her. Suppose she confided in him, and he was understanding and sweet, but nothing more? His ultimate rejection might crush her.

She was mulling over the hopelessness of her situation when Maggie O'Connell phoned. "So you're back already," she drawled. "How was your weekend, Caroline?"

Caroline hadn't mentioned either her destination or her companion when she phoned the office on Friday. But, as always, the sharp-witted Maggie had drawn the correct conclusion.

There was no point denying that she had decided to go away with Matthew Lyle. "It was a disaster," she said, sighing.

"Oh? Feel like talking about it?"

"Not really. I just—I didn't want to go through with it, Maggie. I was too afraid of being hurt. Matthew kept pressing me, and I ended up telling him that Clay was sick when I married him and that we hadn't slept together. He was furious. He thought . . ." Her voice trailed off. She didn't want to repeat what Matthew had assumed.

"I get the picture. He thinks you married Clay Spencer for his money and celebrated for days when he died," Maggie said. "Why didn't you set him straight, Caroline?"

"Because I care too much. The more involved I am, the more hurt I'll end up. Matthew wants me, but he's never been in love with anyone and there's no reason to think I'll be the first."

"But if you don't take a chance . . ."

Caroline knew that. She was weary of thinking about it. "Did the annual report come in from the printer's yet, Maggie?" she asked.

The change of subject was a dismissal, and Maggie took it good-naturedly. "Yes, late Friday afternoon. It looks beautiful, Caroline. You can look forward to seeing it." The two women exchanged goodbyes and hung up.

A short time later Joey Symington's sister Lindsay called. Caroline had barely said hello when the teen-ager burst into gushing expressions of gratitude. "The girls'll just *die* when I tell them you said yes," she prattled. "They've all seen your picture in the paper. I can't wait for the first practice."

Caroline was not aware of having given any commitment to Joey, but obviously the young man had conveyed an entirely different impression to his sister. Then again, Lindsay Symington was only one of a dozen girls, and there was no particular reason for Caroline to meet up with her father. The idea of coaching was appealing to her, and she would have acceded to Joey's request had he been any other boy. It was senseless to back out simply because he was related to Matthew.

"The principal says we can use the gym on Tuesday and Thursday evenings from seven until eight-thirty, Carrie," Lindsay told Caroline, going on to give her directions to Clyde Hill High School.

"I'll see you on Tuesday, then," Caroline replied, mustering her sternest tone. "And tell your friends they should come prepared to work. You can't be a good ball player if you sit on your fanny all day and eat chocolate bars. I hope you girls are in good shape."

Lindsay was apparently unimpressed by Caroline's efforts at authoritarianism. She giggled and promised to warn her teammates that their new coach intended to be, as she put it, "tight" with them.

Caroline smiled to herself and hung up the phone. It was only human to look forward to her new role as volunteer coach. The adulation of Lindsay Symington and her friends would be a pleasant change from the draining tension of worrying about Matthew Lyle's next move and the more general pressures of daily business.

The next day was so ordinary that the dramatic events of the weekend began to seem unreal. Caroline's heart knocked erratically against her rib cage every time her phone buzzed, but all of the calls dealt with routine business matters. It was only logical to expect that Matthew would proceed with his takeover bid, and Caroline wondered why he was denying himself the pleasure of duly informing her of that fact. He certainly wasn't too much of a gentleman to relish making her squirm.

As she glanced through the slick pages of EBE's annual report, she felt unaffected pride in herself and her company. Last year had been a good one—especially given their heavy expenditures for research and development. This year would be even better. She had received unofficial word that one of the anticipated weapons contracts had come through. Based on that news, Sam Hanover had drafted a glowing estimate of earnings and expenses for the first six months of this year, and the figures would be included as a special insert to the main report. Both would be mailed as soon as official confirmation was received. It was unfair that deflated stock prices should outweigh all other considerations in the shareholders' decision as to whether to sell out to Olympia Industries. Caroline hoped that enough of them would share her viewpoint to give her the fifty-one percent she needed.

During the next week her only unpleasant moment came on Tuesday morning, when Sam Hanover marched himself into her office and curtly demanded a progress report on her negotiations with Matthew Lyle. It was unlike Sam to demand anything. Over the last year he had been unfailingly deferential and courteous. Caroline excused his behavior by telling herself that he was under enormous pressure. She hated to deceive him, but could not bring herself to be honest about their position. In a purposely vague answer, she led him to believe that matters were proceeding favorably and promised to keep him informed.

As she exchanged her fawn-colored silk suit for a T-shirt, shorts, and sneakers on Tuesday evening, Caroline found herself looking forward to the workout ahead. And it turned out that Lindsay and her friends, while woefully short of experience, made up for their lack of skill with an infectious enthusiasm and energy. Caroline put the girls through fifteen minutes of warm-up exercises, then stood with a suitably solemn look on her face as each of them demonstrated her prowess or, more often, her lack of it.

For the rest of the practice she broke the girls into two teams and had them play a game. Meanwhile, at the other end of the gym, she took each girl aside and worked with her individually. She concentrated on their shooting, trying to show them what they were doing wrong, and was gratified by the immediate improvement in most of them.

The high school, Lindsay had told Caroline, had not fielded a girls' basketball team for the last several years. Although Lindsay had tried to recruit a few of her friends to form a team, there had been no coach and insufficient interest. Then, the previous week, Joey's friend Brad had come over to dinner. He had perked up his ears when Joey's parents began to discuss Caroline. Distant and cold? he had repeated incredulously. No way! Maybe she was a little shy and reserved, but basically she was terrific, just like one of the guys, and a super ball player to boot.

It was all Lindsay had needed to hear. The next day she had again approached her best friend, saying that she could get the glamorous Caroline Spencer for their coach. They could begin practicing now for next fall. Caroline was amused that Lindsay had promised her services and pleased to be the major inspiration for the fourteen girls who had shown up at this initial session. She hoped that, even if they had joined because of sheer hero worship of the coach, they would continue to come for the exercise and satisfaction the sport brought them.

As they were getting ready to leave the gym, Lindsay called out, "Carrie, would you mind giving me a ride home? It's right on your way."

Caroline was too quick not to recognize a setup when she encountered one. Lindsay might have asked a dozen of her friends, all of whom lived in the area. Nonetheless, she smilingly agreed, intending to decline the inevitable invitation to come in for coffee.

But Janet Symington, Lindsay's mother, was one step ahead of her. She was waiting at the end of the brick walkway when Caroline pulled up and tapped on her window as soon as the car stopped.

Lindsay and Caroline got out of the car. "Go on into the house, Lindsay," Janet instructed her daughter. She waited until the girl was opening the front door before turning her attention to Caroline. "I'm Lindsay's mother, Janet. Come into the house for a glass of wine and let us get to know you," she coaxed.

"It's nice to meet you, Janet, but honestly, it's been a long day," Caroline refused politely. "Maybe some other time."

Janet refused to be put off. "It's only nine o'clock, Carrie. If you're worried about running into my husband, don't be. He's out of town. Besides" —she slanted her a teasing smile—"don't you want to know what Cousin Matt is up to?"

Of course she did. In the first place, her emotions were involved; in the second, only a fool would turn down inside information. Then again, it was doubtful that Janet Symington would actually be willing to offer any. Caroline's silence signified only indecision, but Janet took it for disapproval.

"I was only kidding. I'm sorry if I offended you. Please come in for just a little while, Carrie." She held out a hand. "I just felt a drop of rain. It's probably going to pour. You wouldn't want me to get soaked, would you? Because I won't give up."

"A family characteristic," Caroline muttered, opening the car door again to roll up the window. She added more graciously. "A hot cup of coffee would be nice."

"Good! You know, Matt's father and Joe's mother are brother and sister. Between Matt and Joe, either I developed some tenacity of my own or I got squashed!" she related cheerfully.

A flash of lightning followed a sharp crack of thunder; large droplets of rain splattered down onto the car, the ground, and the two women. They began to laugh and quickly ran inside the Symingtons' contemporary house. It was two stories, furnished with a mixture of comfortable but expensive modern pieces and nineteenth-century antiques.

Janet led Caroline through the living room, around a partition, and into the kitchen. Whoever had designed

128

this house disliked doors; it had an unusually open floor plan. Joey and Lindsay put in a brief appearance and then went up to their rooms to study.

"I've been dying to meet you, and I don't mind admitting it," Janet said as she poured two mugs of coffee. She was certainly a forthright woman, Caroline thought with approval—rather like Maggie O'Connell. You would always know where you stood with her. "I wanted to see the lady who has Matt tied up in knots. Your public persona may be the cool, hard-headed businesswoman, but Brad and Joey are always going on about how terrific you are. I think both of them have crushes on you."

"They're just boys," Caroline murmured, aware that she was blushing. Matthew? Tied up in knots? She couldn't be serious.

"I couldn't let you go without thanking you. Lindsay's just thrilled to have you as a coach."

"I like Lindsay and her friends. I'm going to enjoy working with them."

"You know, Carrie," Janet continued conversationally, "every time Matt comes over to dinner—which is at least once a week—he and Joe start in on you and your company. I've never known Matt to be so . . . obsessed . . . with any woman. I don't approve of what I can gather of his methods either. He was impossible when he got back from the San Juans on Saturday. Stormed in here and snatched Joe away for some business trip."

Caroline felt the heat and color drain from her face. How much *did* Janet Symington know? And why would she speak of something so intimate to Caroline, who was still a virtual stranger?

"I can see I'm making you uncomfortable, and I certainly don't mean to do that, Carrie. I just wanted to tell you that Joe and I are on your side. We think Matt is dead wrong to mix personal relationships with business. He's never done it before, in spite of what you might read in the papers. We'd like to help if we can."

"You can't mean that literally," Caroline blurted out, provoked enough to drop her customary reserve. "Your husband is his cousin. Everyone knows how close they are."

"Of course. What I was trying to say is that we want to make Matt see reason," Janet explained hurriedly. "I have a feeling he just about blackmailed you into going away with him, and if things didn't work out the way he planned, he has only himself to blame."

Caroline wanted to sink through the Solarian floor. Good grief! Did Matthew go around broadcasting bulletins on his amorous adventures to his family?

Her appalled expression must have conveyed her thoughts to Janet, because the other woman colored vividly and mumbled contritely, "Joe's always telling me I talk too much. Matt wouldn't say a word about what happened between the two of you. Unlike me, he's very tight-lipped, and I only found out by accident that you were going up to his island with him. But I can add one and one, Carrie. Last week you were fighting off Matt's takeover attempt, and the next thing I hear, you're partners who go away for secluded weekends together. Besides, Matt . . ." She shut her mouth and chewed on her lower lip.

Caroline, too relieved to wonder what might have come next, managed to thank Janet for the coffee and escape from the house. She supposed the woman meant well; she seemed to be warm and sweet. No doubt she was genuinely grateful to Caroline for coaching Lindsay's team and wanted to help her if she could. But that was hardly a sound basis for a friendship, especially considering who she was related to.

On Thursday, Janet strolled into the gym shortly before the end of practice. Caroline was standing on the sidelines, watching the girls play a game, and couldn't politely ignore her. Mercifully, she merely asked about the girls' progress, sparing Caroline any further speculations, confessions, or offers of help. But just before she left, she drawled nonchalantly, "By the way, Carrie, Matt and Joe are still in Chicago. There's a company there they have their eye on. Seems to me that they'll be so busy with that they won't have much time to fuss around with EBE, even if they succeed with the takeover." She winked and was gone.

The next few weeks produced no dramatic new developments. Caroline heard nothing from Matthew Lyle and was far more disappointed than relieved. The proxy fight continued, at a lazier pace, because it was now apparent that only a minority of the shareholders would mail back signed proxies. As everyone had predicted, the large shareholders attending the annual meeting would decide the fate of EBE.

Caroline forced herself to resume her usual social schedule, accepting invitations to dinner parties and charity events and recruiting escorts from her well-tested list of "safe" older men. She was apprehensive about an accidental meeting with Matthew, but hid it well. Presumably he disliked the social whirl, because they had never met before at any of these functions. He only showed up when business or boats were involved.

As the weeks passed, the Symingtons continued to gently court her friendship. When there was no further mention of anything personal, Caroline found herself slowly letting down her barriers with them. Either Janet or Joe invariably appeared in the gym a few minutes before the end of practice, ostensibly to pick up Lindsay. They were the only parents who ever came inside—all the others waited in their cars in the parking lot—so it was obvious that fetching Lindsay was merely a convenient excuse.

The first time Caroline saw Joe walk in, a week after the initial session, she stiffened with embarrassment. But he only nodded pleasantly but distantly and asked her about the difference between men's and women's basketball. After listening to Caroline's reply, he went on to make a few trenchant observations about her charges. Within ten minutes Caroline found herself joking with him as though they had known each other for years. Another week went by before Janet invited her back to the house for coffee, and by now she was happy to accept. She told herself that the Symingtons were simply Lindsay's parents; any other relationship was irrelevant.

Joe and Janet tactfully avoided any mention of business. Topics ranged from the suddenly balmy spring weather to Lindsay's progress as a basketball player. It seemed quite natural for Caroline to tell them a little about herself, including the fact that she had once considered coaching as a career but had switched to business administration at the wish of her late husband. She was unaware of how wounded she sounded when she spoke of Clay Spencer.

She would have liked to banish Matthew from her thoughts, but she found it impossible. During the daytime she was too busy to fret, but late at night, lying in bed, she would remember the way he had kissed her and touched her, and her body would ache for a repeat performance. She was ashamed of such feelings, cer-

Within minutes, Caroline followed him out of the suddenly oppressive office. Maggie made no comment as Caroline passed by her desk.

To match her mood, Caroline thought as she left the building, the day should have been dank and stormy, not crisp and bright. She set out briskly toward the waterfront, with no particular destination in mind, impatient when the steep pitch of the streets forced her to slow her pace. This general area was Seattle's birthplace, but the original streets of that settlement were some 18 feet below where she was walking. When she reached Pioneer Square, she sat down on a bench under the glass-roofed, wrought-iron, restored Victorian pergola at First and Yesler.

Following the Seattle fire of 1889, the streets of the city had been rebuilt on a level with the second story of the buildings in order to avoid the problems they'd had earlier with mud and backed-up sewage. Initially, the residents of the day had entered their favorite shops and public houses by climbing down flights of steps to the sidewalks, which remained at the original street level. But eventually the sidewalks were raised up as well, with thick glass skylights installed so that pedestrians on the original sidewalks below could see. This "underground" area was dank and cold, however, and the first floors of the original buildings soon became basements, with new entrances constructed at the new street level. The entire underground had been condemned by city authorities many years ago and closed up, and at the present time visitors could inspect the catacomblike passages only by taking a special guided tour.

Caroline watched one of these groups disappear through a wooden door at street level, down the flight of stairs beyond. People sometimes sneaked onto the tour, perhaps ignored by the good-natured guides, and Caroline was briefly tempted to do the same. Unfortunately, high heels and a silk dress were not the proper attire for subterranean explorations.

So she sat and analyzed Sam Hanover's behavior instead. She was saddened that a man she had liked and admired was capable of making such a threat. Would he really carry it out, implicating her rather than admitting sole responsibility for the payoffs? Perhaps she should consult an attorney, but such an action seemed premature. There was still a chance that Sam had buried all evidence of fraud so carefully among the endless columns of corporate expenditures that even Joe Symington would fail to sniff out anything suspicious.

Caroline decided to do nothing, at least for the time being. She certainly wasn't about to arrange another meeting with Matthew. They had nothing left to say to each other.

When she walked back into her office, Maggie followed her through to her desk. "Have a pleasant walk, Caroline?" she asked.

Caroline knew that sly expression only too well. "You heard, didn't you?"

"Maybe I shouldn't have listened, but I did. I didn't like the way Sam barged in here," Maggie said, taking a seat. "What are you going to do?"

"Nothing. I think I'd rather go to jail than try to bail him out." She sighed and smoothed a stray strand of hair. "Anyway, I wasn't cut out for illicit weekends on private islands, Maggie. I'm sorry I ever told you about the payoffs. It might open you up to some kind of conspiracy charge."

"We'll both run to our attorneys after the annual

meeting," Maggie said, smiling. "I'd say it's too early to panic."

"Next month then." Caroline managed a smile in return and pulled several file folders out of her "in" box.

The flowers were delivered that evening—a dozen long-stemmed yellow roses, the enclosed card reading simply "M.L." Caroline couldn't pretend that *they* were strictly business too. She blushed at the thought that Matthew's temper might have cooled, allowing his desire for her to come into play once more.

She was disappointed when Tuesday brought no phone call. Were the flowers some kind of joke then? She didn't want to believe that Matthew would be that cruel. She knew she was a fool for wanting so badly to see him, and her insecurity only added to her tenseness.

She was brisker than usual with the girls at practice, but they treated her snapped-out commands as a huge joke, apparently having decided that she was merely trying to instill some discipline into an unruly crew. Joe Symington came to pick up Lindsay that evening, almost immediately asking Caroline, "See Sanderson's column yesterday?"

It was the first time he had ever alluded to business, and Caroline was determined not to make a fool of herself when she answered. "Yes," she said calmly. "It was a nice vote of confidence in me and my management team."

She noted Joe's subsequent grin with chagrin. "Not really. Although the annual report *was* good, Carrie—I won't say it wasn't. Even so, Matt normally brings in at least a few new people when we take over a company."

"Assuming you win the proxy fight."

"We both know that Olympia Industries is going to win." Caroline could cheerfully have poured the rest of her can of soda over Joe's head. Why did the blasted man have to smile at her disgruntled expression? "You know, Carrie, Matt's never made a pledge of noninterference in an unfriendly acquisition before. Not once. He's not saying why he made an exception in your case, but I can hazard a pretty good guess."

"Oh?" Caroline felt a warm flush creeping up her neck. "What?"

"You know exactly what I mean, or you wouldn't be blushing. By the way," he added with a wink, "Matt's in L.A. for a few days. He didn't much want to go, either. He's been grumpy as the dickens all month, and now that he's finally made up his mind . . ."

They stood side by side and watched the girls trot off the court. Caroline couldn't bring herself to ask Joe to finish the sentence. "How about some coffee, Carrie?" he invited. "I promise, no more teasing."

"Not tonight, Joe."

"Thursday then," he insisted. "We'll talk about the weather if you want."

Caroline couldn't help the smile on her face. "Sure. I'll bring Lindsay home with me." Perhaps she was an idiot to feel so elated, but Joe had made it pretty clear that Matthew wanted to see her, and the feeling was mutual. She didn't want to believe that his motivation was pure lust.

She was certainly not so physically irresistible that an experienced man of the world like Matthew Lyle would be captivated by her to the point of letting his desire interfere with business. His emotions must be involved—at least a little bit—or so she hoped. As for herself, she only wanted the chance to discover how she

138

really felt. She might be wary of falling in love, but even love would be better than the uncertainty that endlessly preoccupied her these days.

Practice went unusually well on Thursday. Even Joey, who had come along to watch, admitted that he was impressed.

"I'll take you out for ice cream," Caroline offered as they walked to the car.

Lindsay and Joey exchanged a brief glance. "We've both got a lot of homework, Carrie. We'd better do it some other time," Joey replied.

"Okay, but you guys must be sick!" As Caroline drove to the Symingtons, she found herself looking forward to sitting down over coffee and bragging a little about the girls' progress. By next fall they would be able to give the other local teams some formidable competition.

"We had a terrific practice," she said to Janet as soon as the other woman opened the door. "The girls . . ."

Her voice trailed off as she noticed Matthew Lyle standing in the living room just beyond the front hall, watching her with an unreadable expression on his face.

Chapter Eight

He was wearing a three-piece pin-striped business suit, his shirt partially unbuttoned, the tie stuffed into his jacket pocket. Caroline felt almost naked in her own brief shorts and clinging T-shirt. Now she knew why Joey and Lindsay had been in such a hurry to get home. They hadn't wanted to keep Cousin Matt waiting. The two of them had mysteriously disappeared, along with their mother, leaving Carrie alone with Matthew. She had been set up.

"Hi," she said, the greeting uncertain and breathless. "The flowers were beautiful. Thank you."

"I'm glad you liked them." His eyes traveled from her sneaker-clad feet to her disarrayed hair and settled on her face. "Joe told me you'd be here tonight. I wanted to speak to you," he said.

"He told me you were in Los Angeles." Caroline was trying for sophistication and failing miserably. "You— you could have called. The office, I mean. Or at home." She clamped her lips together, embarrassed at the way she was babbling.

"I wanted to see you in person." He took several steps toward the door, stopping about two feet away from her. "Joe and Janet will forgive us if we don't stay for coffee. In fact, they'd be surprised if we did. Drive me home, Carrie."

She felt his closeness all too tangibly. Flames licked at her body, touching all the places that Matthew had once caressed. "Wh–where's your car? Isn't it—I mean . . ."

"Being serviced. I came home with Joe." He took her by the arm. "Let's get out of here, Carrie."

He led her to the car, opening up the passenger door for her and helping her inside. Caroline's hand was shaking as she handed him her keys, making them jingle against each other. Suppose he asked her to come inside his house? What was she going to say? The way he had looked at her, he wasn't about to take no for answer.

He lived out on Hunt's Point, only a few miles from the Symingtons' Clyde Hill residence. His house was one of the beautiful colonial-style mansions that were hidden from the single road on that narrow spit of land by high screens of foliage. Light from a three-quarter moon relieved the darkness in the car as he swung into the curved drive and drove up to the front door. Caroline caught a glimpse of a road leading down to a jetty, with Lake Washington beyond.

"Do you—do you keep a boat down there?" she asked hoarsely, needing to break the unbearably tense silence.

"At the yacht club. Two of them" was the brusque reply. He slid over toward Caroline, placing his hand over her own when she started to lift the door handle to get out of the car.

"Don't run away." He touched her face lightly to turn her head. "You shouldn't be allowed out of the house looking like that." His eyes dropped to her breasts, firm and taut under the T-shirt, her flimsy bra doing absolutely nothing to hide the effect he always had on her.

"Unbutton my jacket, Carrie." The sentence, although murmured huskily, was a firm command.

Caroline stared at the buttons, unable to move. She wanted to touch him, to feel his tongue exploring her mouth, but wasn't prepared for the inevitable outcome of such preliminary maneuvers. Matthew took hold of her right hand and placed it against his suit jacket, and somehow her fingers began to clumsily unloop the buttons.

"Now the vest, Carrie." She had felt his heart, slamming rapidly against his chest, and could hear his rasping, hurried breathing. Aroused by his desire for her, she put both hands to work on the smaller buttons of the vest.

He didn't have to mention the shirt. Caroline's fingers got there all by themselves, fumbling inefficiently with the starched material, unhooking three buttons to allow access to his hair-covered chest. She ran her hand lightly over his collarbone, then downward. A moment later Matthew pressed her back against the seat and began to kiss her hungrily, his mouth almost savaging her own. He twined his fingers into her hair, pulling it roughly out of its loose bun, the pins dangling at odd angles. Caroline responded eagerly, too aroused to care about the brief pain he inflicted.

His other hand wedged itself between the seat and

her back, seeking the hook of her bra. He discovered only a smooth length of elastic. He tore his mouth away, pushed up her shirt, and felt the front of her bra. "How does this work?" he muttered.

Caroline couldn't help but smile at his grumpy tone. "It clicks into place. To make a smooth . . ."

"Just undo the bloody thing before I tear it off," he interrupted impatiently.

She did so, her laughter replaced by throaty whimpers when he lowered his head to suck and nibble at each of her nipples in turn. She had never suspected that pleasure could be so intense that she would physically ache from it. She arched her breasts against his mouth, her head thrust back, her lips apart, wantonly welcoming his tongue when at last he raised his head to repossess her mouth. The way he made love to her excited her until she was mindlessly and submissively responsive to him, silently pleading with him to let her give him whatever he wanted. His hands teased her breasts, then wandered elsewhere. His mouth, at first passionate, fierce, and demanding on hers, became almost cruelly teasing, offering light kisses to her neck and face, and only returning to her lips when she moaned his name.

When Matthew released her and moved back to his side of the car, Caroline was confused and out of breath. She stared wordlessly at him.

"You'd better snap that thing back into place before my parents get back," he mumbled hoarsely, buttoning up his shirt.

"Your—your parents?" Didn't they live in Palm Springs? What were they doing in Seattle?

"They're visiting. They got in this afternoon and went out to dinner with some friends." His voice was more even now, a smile tugging at one corner of his mouth. "I can't introduce them to my fiancée when she looks like she'd just been chased through the bushes."

"Your—your what?" Caroline stammered, automatically redoing her bra.

"I want you to marry me, Carrie. You told me that you aren't cut out for an affair, and I accept that. For the last month, ever since we went to the San Juans, I've been trying to forget I ever met you. It didn't work."

Caroline knew that Matthew didn't intend to insult her, but his words lashed her already open wounds. "I wouldn't marry a man who only wants to forget me," she said, turning away from him to hide the tears that suddenly filled her eyes.

"Carrie." His fingers trailed down her arm, causing her to jerk it away from him. "I didn't mean that the way it sounded. I know I said some lousy things to you the last time we were together, but you have to admit I had reason to think what I did. You've got a regular fan club between Joe and Janet, though. They finally convinced me I should stop torturing myself and speak to you."

"Did they convince you to propose, too?" Caroline asked, her taunting tone an attempt to disguise how hurt she felt.

"Give me a break, Carrie. You haven't made it easy for me. It's almost as though you *want* me to have a negative impression of you. Maybe I've figured out what you *aren't;* the problem is that I want to know what you *are.*"

Caroline had been betrayed by too many people she trusted: by her mother, who had died; by her father, who had ignored her; by Clay, who had turned into someone else while she helplessly looked on; and now by Sam Hanover, who was trying to blackmail her. She understood what Matthew was implicitly asking her: Tell me about your marriage. Explain why you never slept with your husband. Make me understand why you're so defensive and wary. But she simply couldn't trust him enough to deliver the answers.

"We'll only become lovers if you refuse," he went on softly. "You know that, Carrie. If I come to your house later tonight, you'll let me in."

"Maybe that would be better. No messy divorce when you get tired of me."

"Damn it, Carrie, how can I know if I'll get tired of you when I don't even know what I feel *now?*" Obviously irritated by her sarcasm, he swung her around to face him. "Listen to me! I'm not being impulsive about this. Our whole relationship's been bizarre, right from the start. I admit that some of that's my fault, but I'm also reasonably perceptive. I've figured out that you don't trust me. I've also figured out that just continuing to see each other won't work. I think you need the security of marriage before you'll let a man get close to you. I *know* I can't take any more physical frustration. Believe me, it doesn't do much for my ego to have to keep seducing you."

Caroline shook her head. "It's insane. Two people can't get married just to find out . . ."

"Why not? I know you don't hate me. Tell me what you *do* feel!" he demanded.

Caroline's eyes dropped to her lap. "I don't know," she whispered. "I'm confused. When you took care of me, the night I got sick, I thought . . ." She couldn't tell him that she had thought she was falling in love with him and then had wondered if it was only an infatuation. "When you touch me . . ." Another sentence impossible to complete, but then she didn't have to. Matthew knew exactly what he did to her.

"Right!" he said curtly. "So *you* tell *me* what we should do!"

Should she agree to his unconventional suggestion? Ever since her experience with Clay, she had looked upon marriage as a long-term jail sentence. Jail sentence? Oh, no, how could she have forgotten about that? If he wanted her enough, would he agree to keep Joe Symington away from the company records?

"Matthew," she began, risking a hesitant look across at him, "if we got married—my company is very important to me—I'd want to run it. . . ."

"We already went through all that. Don't you read the papers?" he snapped.

"I don't like the idea of your cousin poking around . . ."

"Damn it, you're obsessed with that company! What do you want from me, Carrie? An agreement to drop the takeover?"

The possibility of his doing so had never even entered Caroline's head, but a bluff would cost her nothing. She nodded.

"No, Carrie. I can't do that. I promise you a free hand in running EBE any way you want to, but I won't back off on the acquisition. As it is, I'm going to come out of this whole business looking like a lovesick idiot—there's a limit to what my reputation can stand."

She could accept his point of view, but pressed her advantage. "What about Joe, then? Why can't you accept an outside audit?"

"Are you afraid he'll find something you want to keep hidden?" Matthew countered, much too shrewdly.

"Of course not." Caroline was careful to keep her voice level. "It's just that it reflects a lack of confidence in me to tell Joe to pore over . . ."

Mercifully, Matthew interrupted her by lowering his mouth to her lips, kissing her with a puzzling tenderness. "I don't want to argue about it, sweetheart," he said against her mouth. "An audit will satisfy me. I'll keep the bloodhound away if that's what it takes to get a ring on your finger." He drew away and smiled crookedly at her. "You'd better repair the damage before I'm tempted to add to it."

Caroline pulled out the loose hairpins and threw them into her purse. She was running a brush through her hair when the glare of headlights illuminated the interior of the car. The Lyles pulled up behind them; Matthew got out of her car and walked over to greet them. A little while later he walked back, opened the passenger door, and helped Caroline out.

"This is Carrie," he said, his arm around her shoulders pulling her close to him. "Carrie, my parents, Desirée and Henry Lyle."

Henry Lyle, a few inches shorter than his son, the gray strands in his dark hair catching the moonlight, smiled at Caroline and leaned forward to kiss her cheek. "I'm glad to know you, Carrie," he said. "Welcome to the family."

Desirée Lyle was markedly cooler. She inspected Caroline's attire thoroughly, her eyebrows knitted together in bewilderment, then asked her son, "You *did* say Caroline McKay Spencer, didn't you?"

"Carrie coaches Lindsay's basketball team Tuesday and Thursday evenings, Mother. She just came from practice," Matthew explained.

"Really?" Mrs. Lyle's tone was neutral. "I must say, Caroline, you aren't what I was told to expect."

Caroline stood rigidly in Matthew's embrace, embarrassed to the tips of her toes. What had the woman been told? And by whom?

147

"My mother is famous for her bluntness," Matthew remarked. "Let's go inside."

They walked through the slate-floored hallway of the two-story, green-shuttered house, and Matthew ushered everyone into the charming, antique-furnished living room. Caroline silently admired the huge red-brick fireplace and the Oriental carpet on the pegged wood floor. Originals by some very famous French Impressionists hung on the walls of the traditional, yet homey, room.

Caroline assumed that Matthew had inherited the house from his parents, and turned to Mrs. Lyle to compliment her on the room. "This is very lovely," she said. "It's beautiful, and it still has a real warmth to it."

"Thank you. Haven't you seen the house before?" Mrs. Lyle asked her.

"No, Mother," Matthew drawled. "Caroline hasn't seen the living room, and she hasn't seen my bedroom either."

Caroline blushed hotly, her reaction producing the first token of approval from Matthew's mother. She smiled more warmly and said, "Come into the kitchen with me, Carrie. You can help me make coffee."

Caroline followed her back across the hall, through a formal dining room, and into the kitchen. Although the appliances in the room were modern, the floor was red brick and the wallpaper a colonial print. A massive oak table with six chairs around it sat in the center of the room, which seemed perfect for scrumptious Sunday brunches and playpenned infants.

Desirée Lyle measured out the coffee and took some cake from a breadbox built into one of the cabinets. She slid out a tray from a custom-built compartment and flicked open an upper cabinet. "Why don't you fetch down some mugs, Caroline? They're a little high for me to reach."

Caroline complied, then sat down with Mrs. Lyle at the table to wait until the coffee was ready.

"You know," Mrs. Lyle said, "Matthew's taken his time about settling down, Carrie. I hope that you'll make him happy. He's my only son and we're very close."

"I'll do my best," Caroline answered. She knew that she was speaking the truth. She wanted nothing more than for both of them to be happy.

"You don't know each other very well, do you?" Caroline was trying to come up with some suitable excuse for their hasty engagement when Mrs. Lyle went on, "I don't suppose I can complain about that. Henry and I eloped after one weekend together."

"Really? You don't . . ." Caroline could have bitten her tongue. How could she have almost blurted out that Matthew's mother seemed anything but impulsive?

"*You* don't either," was the twinkling response. "Matthew didn't join us tonight because he was anxious to see you, you know. So I asked my friend about you, and she said you were a cool, beautiful blonde who dressed like a model."

"Not on a basketball court," Caroline said. Perhaps this woman wasn't quite so intimidating after all. "But I guess I look that way at work."

"Will you continue as president of your company?"

Caroline smiled at the question. "It depends on Matthew, doesn't it? After our annual meeting, he'll be the boss as far as business goes."

Mrs. Lyle pursed her lips. "Modern women!" she scoffed. "I come from a very traditional family, Caroline. My father was quite the patriarch. If I were you, I would answer my question by saying that after the marriage Matthew will be the boss period."

Caroline knew that an honest answer would land her in hot water with her future mother-in-law, but she couldn't bring herself to nod in polite agreement. "I can't accept that sort of arrangement. My independence is important to me. Marriage should be a partnership. When I was married to Clay Spencer . . ." She stopped abruptly. She wasn't about to confide in Matthew's mother.

"Were you happy with him?" The question, so strangely gentle after Mrs. Lyle's no-nonsense scolding, caught Caroline by surprise. She turned away to hide the anguished look in her eyes.

"I'm beginning to see that you are a very complicated young woman, Carrie. If you wouldn't mind answering one more question?"

Caroline, her features once again composed, turned back to Mrs. Lyle. She studied the wistful expression in the older woman's eyes, curious as to the cause of it. "Yes?"

"My daughter has three little boys. As much as I love them, I would like to have a granddaughter to spoil with all the pretty things I could never afford to buy Terry. Henry and I had quite a struggle in the first years of our marriage, Carrie. Is there any hope that you'll give me that granddaughter?"

Good grief, how was she going to answer that? Inside a month, Matthew Lyle might be bored with her. She would have to be insane to think of allowing herself to become pregnant, especially right away. She settled on a diplomatic response. "We've never discussed children, Mrs. Lyle." Unbidden, a tender smile lit up her face. "If we do have a little girl, she'll probably end up even taller than I am. It will cost you a fortune to keep replacing everything she outgrows!"

Desirée Lyle seemed pleased by her response. "I can always sell some Olympia stock," she said, rising to switch off the coffee maker and place the pot on the tray. Caroline picked it up and followed her into the living room.

Henry Lyle was sitting on a sofa opposite the fireplace, his son on the adjacent love seat. When Matthew held out his hand to Caroline, she set the tray on the coffee table and obediently sat down next to him. Her body blazed into life when he began to feather his fingers absentmindedly up and down her arm.

"So when's the wedding?" Mr. Lyle asked Matthew.

His wife didn't give her son the opportunity to answer. "There's so much to do," she fretted. "We'll have to see when the country club is available, Henry. I wish we weren't going to the Far East. I don't see how it can take place before next fall."

Matthew shook his head. "No way, Mother. We're getting married before you leave for Japan." And then, when his mother looked positively scandalized by such unseemly haste, he drawled, "I don't want to shock you, Mother, but enforced celibacy is taking its toll on me. I'm not waiting."

Henry Lyle burst out laughing, his amusement only intensified by his wife's horrified, *"Really,* Matthew!"

"Really, Mother!" he mocked. "I seem to have heard that Dad had you quite legally married inside of forty-eight hours. Your three hundred-odd society pals can come to a belated reception if you want to toss us one."

Mrs. Lyle studied her son's implacable expression for mere seconds before delivering a Gallic shrug. Soon afterward, Matthew walked Caroline out to her car, taking her in his arms and kissing her good night with a leashed passion that tempted her to invite him home. "We'll take care of the arrangements tomorrow," he said. "I'll come by your office and take you to lunch first. If you have an appointment, cancel it."

Caroline drove back to Mercer Island in a daze. Could all this have happened in one brief evening? Was she really going to marry a virtual stranger?

She knew the answer to both questions was yes. Even if there had been no Sam Hanover and no threat of prison, she still would have said yes. When Matthew took her in his arms, she had no power to deny him what both of them wanted.

Hunger for him overrode both her common sense and her doubts. She knew it was a risk to marry a man she barely knew—dangerous to become the wife of someone she didn't trust. A part of her wanted desperately to confide in him, to tell him about Clay and about the payoffs that threatened to explode into a corporate scandal. But she simply couldn't. He wasn't in love with her. He might not protect her. The idea that Matthew might be willing to let her take her chances with the authorities was far more devastating to her than the thought of going to jail.

Their engagement became public knowledge the day before Caroline issued a formal announcement. SEATTLE TYCOON TO WED TAKEOVER TARGET, one front-page headline proclaimed. Sanderson's coy story on them was entitled "Love in the Boardroom." Caroline suspected that the source of the leak was the garrulous jeweler who had sold them their simple gold wedding bands and the exquisite sapphire and diamond engagement ring she now wore on her left ring finger.

Their trip to the jewelry store had followed the promised lunch, a surrealistic affair during which they calmly discussed wedding arrangements with all the nonchalance of a couple engaged for years. A marriage license was the next order of business.

When she returned, Caroline took Maggie O'Connell into her office, announced that she was marrying Matthew, and asked her to be the matron of honor. Maggie asked no questions. She accepted with pleasure, saying that she hoped everything would turn out well and that Caroline must do whatever she thought best. Caroline promptly hugged her, touched that her friend was making no judgments.

The next morning they had gone over to one of Seattle's most elegant stores to shop for dresses for the ceremony. Caroline chose a long-sleeved A-line silk crêpe de chine dress in a pastel blue-green; it had tiny cloth-covered buttons with loop closings down the back and at each cuff. Maggie loved the way the color looked on her, just as Caroline adored Maggie's light mint, empire-style dress. "If only you would say yes to Jerry," Caroline teased, "we could do this all over again, with the same dresses."

"I've been thinking about it," Maggie admitted. "Maybe you and Matthew will inspire me to give in."

The wedding was scheduled for the following Friday morning. Caroline saw Matthew almost every night, but always in the company of friends, relatives, and business colleagues. Desirée Lyle had been deprived of her elaborate reception, but she made up for it by inviting half of Seattle to join them for cocktails, dinner, or nightcaps during the week before the wedding.

Caroline handled these affairs with her usual sophisticated charm and admired Matthew's easy warmth with these people. The more she watched him, the more impressed she was. He was both intelligent and compelling. People listened to him when he talked, but the reverse was just as true. She wished she could be as open and relaxed as her fiancé.

Late each night he would walk her to her car, limiting his good night kiss to a mere brush of his lips over hers. Even this brief contact seared Caroline's body with frustration. If Matthew felt the same way, he never said so.

Of all Caroline's colleagues and acquaintances, Sam Hanover was most delighted by the news of her engagement. He came into her office in the middle of the week to offer his gleeful congratulations, but Caroline cut him short with a curt, "He said he would stay away from our records, Sam. Please excuse me. I have work to do."

Sam had left, but not before saying acidly, "I used to feel sorry for you when you were married to Clay, but you're as ruthless as they come, Carrie. You should have been a man."

Caroline invited a number of her friends and colleagues to the wedding. Sam Hanover was not among them.

On the day of their wedding, just after Matthew helped Caroline into his car and started toward the church where they were to be married, the overcast skies stopped threatening rain and began to produce it. Caroline buttoned her raincoat all the way up and pulled the hood over her French-pleated hair. Matthew, wearing a dark blue suit, white shirt, and striped tie, held an umbrella over her head as both of them hurried into the building.

Several dozen friends and relatives watched them

exchange their vows, among them Matthew's sister Terry and her family, who had flown in from Maine the previous day. Caroline made her responses in a soft, unsteady voice and tipped her head back anxiously for Matthew's kiss at the end of the ceremony. He stared down into her eyes, murmured, "I don't know how I'm going to wait until tonight," and took her mouth in a lingering, sensuous kiss that left her aching for more.

The rest of the day was just as interminable for Caroline. After the ceremony, everyone went back to the Lyle house for a catered buffet lunch arranged by Matthew's mother. She had refused to let Caroline handle any of the details that were normally the province of the bride and her family, saying that Caroline was far too busy to be troubled with them. Caroline was grateful for her help, but could not do justice to the beautiful French food Mrs. Lyle had procured.

It was late afternoon by the time Matthew and Caroline drove his parents and his sister's family down to Sea-Tac Airport. All of them were flying back to California for the weekend. The Lyles would be leaving for the Orient the following Monday.

EBE's annual meeting was scheduled for Wednesday morning, Olympia Industries' annual meeting for the beginning of June, so Matthew and Caroline had agreed to take a honeymoon later in the summer. Back at Matthew's house, he unlocked the door, swept Caroline into his arms, and carried her across the threshhold. The gesture pleased her, but when he continued straight up the stairs to his bedroom she became rather alarmed.

"Don't look so petrified," he said huskily, putting her down next to the king-sized bed. He turned her around and studied the back of her dress. "Did you pick this out because you remembered that I like to unbutton buttons or just to reduce me to half-crazed frustration?"

"Neither. Maggie said she liked the color on me," Caroline answered, her voice unsteady.

"You would look beautiful in a burlap sack, Mrs. Lyle." He began to unfasten the buttons, but as Caroline had discovered, it was an arduous task. Before long he was cursing under his breath. "I'm going to rip this thing off!" he growled.

"Matthew, it cost a fortune!" Caroline protested.

"So I'll buy you a dozen more of them!" In spite of his threat, he continued to struggle with the tiny buttons, turning Caroline into his arms when he had finished. "Now take it off for me," he commanded, his dark eyes burning into hers.

"I can't." Caroline stepped back and wiggled her wrists, unable to suppress a giggle. "The buttons on the sleeves, Matthew . . ."

An ill-tempered curse sliced the air. Matthew dealt with the four buttons on each cuff and slid the dress off Caroline's shoulders, letting it fall to the floor. He divested her of her slip and panty hose with cool efficiency. "Thank heaven," he drawled, observing the delicate underwear she had on. "I was expecting another diabolical brassiere—maybe even a chastity belt."

But when he took her back into his arms his sense of humor vanished. The initial light kiss they exchanged soon deepened into a completely mutual and wildly passionate embrace. Caroline's fears were replaced by an aching hunger that made her teasingly bold.

She unclasped her hands from behind Matthew's neck and put them against his chest to push him away. "Why," she said, purring seductively, "am I the only one in this room who's half naked?" She began to loosen his tie.

By now, Matthew was far too aroused to stand still while Caroline undressed him. He quickly stripped off his clothing, tossing it across a convenient chair. Caroline watched, fascinated by the lithe, muscled frame now displayed in front of her.

Matthew noticed her stare and smiled crookedly. "Feel free to touch," he drawled. He picked her up, swept back the covers on the bed, and lay her between the sheets. Her remaining garments were quickly removed, their bodies pressed together intimately. Matthew's hands and mouth left a trail of fire as they caressed her skin. Within moments, Caroline heard herself moan, "Matthew—please—love me."

Chapter Nine

"I'm sorry, Carrie."

Caroline, lying on her side with her back to Matthew, instinctively flinched when his hand stroked her shoulder. He had been as restrained and sensitive as any woman could have wished, continuing to arouse her even after she pleaded with him to take her. She had thought herself ready for his possession, but her body had resisted. After long minutes of frustration, his control had simply snapped. For Caroline, the result had been both painful and unsatisfying.

"I haven't looked at another woman since I met you, Carrie. It's been months." His voice was gentle as he tried to make her understand what had happened. "I didn't want to hurt you, sweetheart, but I couldn't stop. It will be better for you next time."

Next time? She didn't want to think about a next time. "Please just leave me alone," she sobbed, not caring if he saw the tears that were now soaking her pillow.

"Okay. Half an hour," he muttered, rolling off the bed and padding out of the room. Caroline soon stopped crying and began to consider what he had told her. Had there really been no other women since the day they had met? Matthew had no reason to lie about something like that; it must be true. She was acting like a child, lying up here and condemning him. She pulled a robe from her suitcase and went downstairs to find him.

He was sitting at the kitchen table, drinking a glass of wine, so immersed in his own thoughts that he failed to notice Caroline until she softly called his name.

"I won't touch you again until you want me to, Carrie." His expression was unsmiling, his eyes guarded.

"I—I overreacted," Caroline admitted. "It never occurred to me that you hadn't—that there weren't other women."

He reached out his hand, his gaze warmer now, and Caroline stepped forward to take it. "I've been too obsessed with *you*. Hadn't you noticed?" A smile slowly took possession of his mouth.

"Like Cascade Mining, you mean?" Caroline blurted out.

He began to laugh. "Which of them told you that? Joe? Janet?"

"Joey. I wasn't flattered, being compared to a mining company."

"But there's a lot of truth in it. I tend to be single-minded when I go after something." He took in her hurt expression and quickly added, "I wanted you much more than I wanted Cascade Mining, Carrie. I still do."

"Physically, you mean."

"Yes. Emotionally, you still keep me at a distance. I don't want to start another argument by asking the same old questions."

Caroline felt that by even raising the issue he was implicitly questioning her. She slipped her hand out of his grasp and sat down at the table.

They spent a quiet evening. Together, they fixed a light dinner—omelets and a tossed salad—and then sat down in the den to read through office paperwork. Matthew's good-night kiss was a careful peck on the forehead, and he slept far to the left in the king-sized bed. Caroline's emotions were frazzled; she was grateful for his consideration.

On Saturday they borrowed a neighbor's pickup and drove to Mercer Island to collect Caroline's clothing and a few other personal possessions. When she had the time, she would sort through the rest of her belongings, then rent the house. If the marriage foundered, it would stand waiting for her return.

Later, they took a leisurely drive eastward into the Cascade Mountain range, shared a picnic lunch, then returned home. They talked mostly of Matthew's business career. He freely admitted that he loved the intricate maneuverings involved in forced acquisitions. Caroline was fascinated by the stories he told her. At one point he remarked disarmingly, "I suppose it was the same with you. It was a novelty—having a woman fight me off. It made me want you twice as much."

Caroline wondered what would happen when the human takeover was complete. She was still confused about her feelings, sure she was in love with him one moment, yet too wary to admit it the next. The fact was, he didn't love *her,* and she could never lose sight of that.

After dinner and a TV movie, she went up to bed while Matthew stayed downstairs to work. He had been sensitive to her wishes and had made no move to touch her all day. Although she still found him potently sensuous and would have welcomed his kisses and caresses, she wasn't ready to let him make love to her completely. She wanted to set the pace. Perhaps she was testing him unfairly, but she couldn't seem to help it.

She was only half awake when he came into the darkened bedroom and felt no sense of alarm when he got into bed next to her. Her eyes flew open when he nuzzled her shoulder. Then his hand moved along the length of her body and slipped underneath her nightgown to explore her breast.

"Matthew, please," Caroline protested. "You said . . ."

"I know what I said," was the hoarse response. "But I'm not a block of wood, Carrie. You're my wife. I want you."

His mouth gently grazed her lips. Caroline's flicker of response was doused by a bitter feeling of betrayal. She lay rigid, suffering his attempts to arouse her. His hands teased her breasts, his mouth wandered over her face. She told herself that she had been a fool to trust him; he was totally selfish, a thoughtless, inconsiderate brute.

Her lack of response angered him into explosive insistence. Caroline struggled fiercely, pushing at his chest and inadvertently scratching him in the process. "Okay, okay!" Matthew said furiously. "I get the message!" He retreated to his side of the bed.

Caroline lay awake, confused and unhappy, long after Matthew's deep, sibilant breaths told her that he was sound asleep. She was angry at him for making advances and felt guilty about refusing them. It was almost two in the morning when she finally dozed off.

Tormenting, surrealistic dreams erupted from her unconscious mind. She was eighteen. She met Matthew Lyle at a yacht race; the two fell wildly in love with each other. She was in a chapel on his boat, dressed in a pristine white bridal gown. Clay Spencer was walking her down the aisle, her arm hooked through his. Matthew, her groom, stood waiting next to a black-robed minister. Then Clay and Matthew began to scream at each other. Matthew grabbed her arm and dragged her to the altar. Clay stormed from the room, swearing at both of them, and jumped from the boat.

It was nighttime. Caroline was waiting in bed for Matthew. She closed her eyes dreamily, and opened them only when she heard him open the door. But somehow she was in the wrong bed—Clay's bed, in Clay's house. And Clay was walking toward her. She bolted up and screamed out Matthew's name, but Clay continued his menacing, relentless march to the bed. Caroline screamed when he touched her, fighting him frantically.

"No! Get away from me! I hate you!" She pummeled at his chest, but her hands were captured before they could do any damage. Her eyes, full of loathing, flew to the face of her tormentor.

It was Matthew, not Clay. She was in Hunt's Point, not Mercer Island. And Matthew was looking down at her, his face absolutely stricken. Caroline began to sob with relief and almost collapsed against his body. "Oh, Matthew," she moaned. "I had another nightmare. I dreamt I was married to you, but it was Clay—he was trying to . . ."

Soothing hands massaged her back and head until the

tears stopped falling. "Carrie," Matthew pleaded, "please. Tell me why you have nightmares about Clay."

She was too distraught to argue. "I made myself do whatever he wanted. I felt like I had to. And then you broke your word. I thought I should do what *you* wanted. I confused the two of you."

"Tell me about it, Carrie," he murmured. "Please, sweetheart."

She was still half asleep, her defenses nonexistent. When he held her like this, all her doubts disappeared. She loved him and wanted him to love her. He had to understand that she wasn't a cold-hearted, manipulative gold digger. The story poured out of her.

She started with her awkward childhood, her distant father, how Clay had been kind to her at a time when few people were. By the time she got to her marriage and described the gradual change that had transformed her husband, she was sobbing softly, her words broken and hoarse.

Matthew offered only an occasional exclamation of sympathy, a murmured exhortation to continue. When she was finally finished, he kissed her tenderly on the mouth. "Is there anything else you want to tell me, Carrie?" he asked.

She shook her head, wondering what else there could possibly be. Matthew lay down and pulled her into his arms. "I'll put you back to sleep, sweetheart," he murmured. He began to massage the back of her neck and temples, his fingers deftly working to unknot the tense muscles.

Caroline felt an enormous sense of release. She had never before confronted the fact that part of her detested Clay Spencer. On one level, she thought that made her a terrible person. But she had admitted it to

Matthew tonight and he didn't seem to think that she was evil or ungrateful. As she relaxed against his chest, the memories of those four and a half years grew distant, unimportant. She was momentarily at peace with herself, content to be in Matthew's arms.

Then other sensations intruded as she cuddled close to him, making her suddenly aware of his arousal. Her right hand slid from his neck to his shoulder to his chest, caressing him, and she felt him tremble. She stretched sensuously and rolled onto her back.

"Matthew," she purred, "rub my stomach for me."

He turned onto his side to reach the flat expanse of skin, gently kneaded it. "Feel better?" he murmured.

"Umm." She sighed. When he took his hand away, she protested, "Don't stop." She pulled it back, placing it over her breast.

"Carrie." The name was a strangled moan on his lips. "You don't know what this is doing to me."

"Yes, I do," she whispered, arching against him.

His lovemaking, constrained and deliberate, excited her mercilessly, provoking her into a silent battle with him. She returned his kisses with abandoned passion, her hands roving over his body, determined to undermine his control. And she was only too successful, arousing him to a rough, wild response, his possession deeply satisfying to her.

Afterward, both of them were utterly exhausted. They soon fell asleep in each other's arms, Caroline smiling to herself because all her doubts were finally gone. She loved Matthew, and she had made the right decision in marrying him.

She woke to the smell of fresh coffee, to the feel of Matthew's lips on hers, to the sound of his husky, "Good morning."

Her lips curved into a smile, her eyes still closed. "What are we going to do today?"

"The weather is beautiful. We could go sailing. Or we could stick to indoor sports," he drawled, sitting down on the bed next to her, placing the mug of coffee on the night table.

Caroline slanted him an innocent look. "Indoor sports?" she teased. "You mean get some *real* exercise? Like basketball?"

"Are you complaining about last night?" he challenged.

She twined her arms around his neck. "Yes. It was very disappointing. I thought you said you were such a great lover." She grinned impishly at him.

"I was saving the good stuff for today." he informed her, pushing her gently down onto the soft pillows. In truth, Caroline doubted that there could be anything more to learn. Matthew spent the day showing her how wrong she was.

Caroline sailed into her office on Monday morning still glowing from Sunday night.

"Marriage obviously agrees with you," Maggie observed dryly. "In fact, you're a positive inspiration. How would you like to be a matron of honor next month?"

Caroline, blushing and smiling all at the same time, rushed over to enfold Maggie in a hug. "For you, I'd even delay my honeymoon," she said. "Tell me all about it."

Maggie did so, admitting that she had finally realized that Jerry was very different from her first husband, and that there was no need to punish one for the sins of the other. The two women celebrated her engagement with a champagne lunch late that morning. When Caroline returned to her office, her thoughts were on Matthew. She was able only to skim her work.

Impatient to see him, she left early and arrived home to find him seated in the plushly carpeted den, glancing through a stack of annual reports. She dropped into his lap, not waiting for an invitation, and kissed him on the mouth. His answering passion reassured her that his desire for her had not waned, and the evening followed the pattern set over the weekend.

Tuesday was equally idyllic. Caroline was not so bewitched by her newly discovered love for Matthew that she overlooked the fact that his feelings for her were of another, less intense, sort, but she told herself that he needed time to get to know her. He was still too physically obsessed with her to be interested in lengthy conversations, and since Caroline enjoyed every minute of their lovemaking, she could hardly protest. Through her actions, she would show him that she was warm and loving. It was true that she wouldn't be truly happy until her feelings were returned, but she allowed herself to hope that it would be only a matter of days, or perhaps weeks, until he felt an emotional commitment to her.

On Wednesday, precisely at ten in the morning, Caroline pounded a gavel down on the rectangular table set up at the front of a large conference room in a downtown Seattle hotel and called EBE's annual meeting to order. Her eyes sought Matthew's; he was seated in the front row and smiled encouragement at her.

The first item on the agenda was her annual report to the shareholders, which she delivered with confidence and enthusiasm. The speech was well received, the applause more than polite. The election of directors followed.

As they lay in bed together that morning, Caroline had hesitantly reminded Matthew that she intended to vote for the current slate of directors. He laughingly told her that he had never expected her to vote herself out of office. Even though the proxies had been counted in advance, it took over an hour to verify the final results. When it was over, Matthew Lyle had won handily with some fifty-nine percent of the vote. The reason for his comfortable margin of victory was obvious: His marriage to Caroline had convinced EBE shareholders that the company no longer seriously opposed a takeover bid.

After the election, Caroline held out the gavel to Matthew, as the new chairman of the corporation. He shook his head. "You finish up, sweetheart. You know more about the agenda than I do."

The remaining business to be transacted concerned a stock option plan and several resolutions introduced by shareholders. These items, as well as the question period, took less than ninety minutes. The new board of directors held a brief meeting afterward to formally vote on the acquisition by Olympia Industries. Caroline was not invited to attend, but then, she already knew the outcome.

She had mixed emotions as she drove home that night. A part of her acknowledged that EBE would thrive as a division of Matthew's conglomerate, but she mourned her company's loss of independence.

"You're very quiet," Matthew remarked over dinner.

Caroline shrugged. "Maybe the company meant more to me than I knew. I'll hate it when you liquidate the nonmilitary division."

"EBE should be broken down into two separate companies, Carrie," he replied. "Your military division has been carrying the corporation. Earnings on nonmilitary systems are too low."

It was not the response Caroline had hoped to hear. She should have known that Matthew would put business before personal considerations. "So you are going to sell it off," she said, her tone dejected.

"I didn't say that. I said your earnings are too low. I'm in business to make a profit, and I expect every one of my companies to contribute to it. I'd need to take a closer look at your operations before making a final decision."

The sentence hung in the air like something tangible. Matthew very deliberately picked up his mug of coffee and sipped, watching for Caroline's reaction. She knew she was trapped. If she didn't let him look at the books, he would sell the division at the end of the year. But if Joe made the type of thorough analysis Matthew was hinting at, he would find out about the bribes Sam had paid.

When she said nothing, Matthew went on evenly, "I'm not criticizing your performance as an executive, and I don't want to sell the division unless I have to. There are people who can help you run it more efficiently, Carrie, but you have to let them in the door."

Caroline played for time—she didn't know what else to do. "When you asked me to marry you, you said . . ."

"I know what I said." He pushed away his cup. "I have a lot of paperwork to do. I'll be in the den."

Caroline watched him walk out of the kitchen. She supposed he was annoyed with her, even though his last words had been matter-of-fact, not curt. After clearing the table and stacking the dishes in the dishwasher, she settled herself in the living room with a collection of humorous essays. Hours later, she peeked in at Matthew, who sat at his desk, surrounded by manila file folders. "I'll be up in a few minutes," he said.

After lying alone in the moonlit bedroom for nearly an hour, Caroline decided that he wasn't coming at all. Perhaps he was angry with her or simply absorbed in his work, but those considerations had never stopped him from wanting her in the past. Was he bored with her already, then, after less than a week of marriage? Miserable and frightened, she found it impossible to sleep.

She didn't pretend to be anything but wide awake when Matthew finally came to bed at almost one thirty in the morning. He stripped and slid under the covers, his eyes on Caroline, who was propped up against several pillows. Without a word, he lowered his head to her mouth, kissing her with a demanding hunger totally different from his lovemaking of the last few days.

Caroline had always appreciated Matthew's innate politeness, a feature of his personality that extended even into the bedroom. He was much more a giver than a taker in bed, concerned first for her pleasure, then for his own. But not tonight.

As always, Caroline responded wantonly to the fierce passion of his embrace. She craved reassurance in the knowledge that he found her physically desirable, if nothing else. His hands caressed her knowingly, but she sensed that his purpose was to dominate, not arouse. His kisses were almost savage in their intensity. If the sensations he aroused in her had been less exquisitely pleasurable, Caroline might have found them a sort of punishment. Loving him, she cooperated in her own subjugation. The fact that Matthew seemed to be almost out of control added a wildly exciting hint of danger to their lovemaking.

Afterward, he murmured her name, turned his back to her, and promptly fell asleep. Caroline, physically fulfilled but emotionally unsettled, wondered if the successful takeover of EBE had acted as some sort of potent aphrodisiac, compelling him to conquer her just as thoroughly as he had conquered company after company.

Matthew's behavior the next morning was so totally ordinary that Caroline decided that her thoughts of the previous night had been much too fanciful. Her experience with men was limited—she had assigned complex motivations to Matthew when he had probably wanted only to finish his work before coming to her, exhausted but unwilling to let her go. Certainly his goodbye kiss was passionate and tender, just as always, and the smile and wave he gave her were the same as earlier in the week.

When she arrived at her office, she soon stopped worrying and got down to work. At noon Matthew and Joe Symington appeared in her office. Caroline automatically assumed they had come to take her to lunch if she was free.

Since she was, she smiled up at both of them. "I have to finish this up. I'll be ready in five minutes."

Matthew's features were stoic. "This is business, Carrie. You'd better come in here, too, Maggie," he called back over his shoulder.

Maggie hurried in, and the two women exchanged a troubled look. Matthew snapped out, "I want to see the corporation's records for the last four years. I want every single piece of paper, ladies—every purchase order, every sales slip, every bill. If we decide to interview any of your employees, I expect their full cooperation. Two of my security men are down at

Hanover's office to make sure he doesn't accidentally lose anything."

Caroline stared at him, stricken into silence. Maggie cocked an eyebrow, silently asking whether the order should be obeyed.

"The action is taken by unanimous vote of the new board, Carrie," Matthew went on, his voice implacable. "Let's get it over with."

Caroline nodded at Maggie. There was no way she could stop him, and she knew it.

Box after box of files was carried out of the building and stacked into a truck parked at the curb. Caroline felt that Matthew had taken her heart and casually tossed it into the same truck, an expendable item. He had led her to believe that he wouldn't interfere in her business, but he had broken his promise without one word of explanation.

She had no patience for Sam's angry threats. When he stormed into her office, she looked him coldly in the eye, rose from her chair, and left the room. When she returned half an hour later, Maggie informed her that he had gone to the Renton plant for the rest of the day.

There was nothing Maggie could do or say to help. Caroline made only one request of her before she left for the day: that she call Lindsay Symington and have the girl cancel practice for that evening. She couldn't face her giggling teenaged brood tonight.

She was tempted to run away, to pack a suitcase and return to the house on Mercer Island. But she was seething with resentment and pain, and longed to confront Matthew. When he finally appeared in the house, it was almost midnight.

Caroline rushed to the front hall as soon as she heard the door open. "Where have you been?" she asked, her voice hoarse with her effort to control her anger.

"Working. Look, Carrie, I'm tired. I—"

"I'll bet you are," Caroline interrupted. How dare he sound so bored, after what he had done to her! "You couldn't wait to have a look at those books, could you?" she accused.

"I wasn't working on EBE. There are more important . . ."

"Is that why you and your cousin stormed in like an invading army? Because it wasn't important?" By now Caroline was screaming at him.

"Calm down. You're getting hysterical."

"How am I supposed to act? Married to a man with no decency, no sense of ethics, whose word isn't worth two cents! How could you touch me the way you did, and call me sweetheart, and hold me—"

Caroline couldn't continue. She was so mortified by the tears that were suddenly rolling down her cheeks that she turned and fled up the stairs.

When Matthew joined her in the bedroom, her emotions were once again under control. She would die before she would let him see her cry again. "You can sleep in the guest room," she said tightly. "I'm not sharing a bed with you."

"Fine." He shrugged. "Maybe you'll cool off by tomorrow."

She could read nothing in his eyes—not anger, not irritation, not even boredom. The minute he left the room, she started to cry again.

Caroline's pain was joined by increasing frustration over the next few days. Matthew continued to sleep in the guest room. He seemed completely indifferent to her, both physically and in every other way, never kissing her, never touching her, never initiating a

172

conversation. When she was finally calm enough to ask him just why he had broken his promise, he said with a yawn, "It's what we usually do when we take over a company. Analyze its operations. EBE's nothing special."

Did he mean to imply that Caroline Spencer was nothing special either? She remembered his lovemaking on Wednesday night. Her first impressions had been right. It must have been the last, triumphant conquest. Matthew had admitted that he enjoyed pursuing elusive objects, especially unwilling ones. Now that he possessed both her and her company, he had lost all interest in both.

As on so many other occasions, Caroline buried her grief and forced herself to continue with her normal schedule. She saved her tears for late at night, when she was alone in bed. She saw very little of Matthew. He was seldom in the house, even during the weekend, and Caroline told herself he must be at his office. It was too painful to picture him in the arms of another woman.

On Tuesday evening she threw all her energy into coaching Lindsay's team, keeping the girls an extra half hour. She tried to avoid speaking to Janet Symington, who was waiting for practice to end, but Janet, as Caroline had learned the first night they met, was nothing if not persistent. When Caroline ignored her and tried to walk out of the gym, Janet rushed over to stop her, actually taking her by the arm to prevent her from leaving.

"Carrie, what's going on? I haven't seen Joe for more than a few hours since last Thursday. He won't say a word about it except that it concerns EBE."

Caroline stiffened, her eyes bitter with disbelief. "You don't know? I thought he told you everything!"

"I swear to you, Carrie, I don't." The distress in Janet's voice sounded so genuine that some of Caroline's hostility faded.

"Your husband and his lying cousin burst into my office last Thursday and carried off all my records. They're dissecting my company."

"But why?"

Caroline shook her head. She didn't know why Matthew and Joe were so determined to check every last piece of corporate paper. "I don't know. Matthew says it's standard procedure, but I don't believe him. He promised he wouldn't do this to me."

"It's *not* standard," Janet confirmed. "Matt must have a good reason."

"Then he hasn't told it to me. We've hardly spoken in four days, Janet."

Janet Symington put her arm around Caroline's waist, the gesture enough to make Caroline's eyes fill with tears. "Come on. I'll walk you to your car," Janet said. As they locked up the building, she added, "I feel terrible about this. I feel that I helped bring the two of you together. I thought you would be so good for each other, and I was sure that Matt was crazy about you."

Caroline brushed away a tear, unable to answer. Janet hesitated only a moment before hugging her. "If there's anything I can do, Carrie, please ask. If I find anything out, I'll call you."

Caroline managed to mumble her thanks, only too aware that neither Janet Symington nor anyone else would ever be able to ease the pain she felt. If she had any pride, she would walk out on Matthew. But she couldn't admit that her marriage was over. She stayed.

Chapter Ten

Four days later, in the middle of the afternoon, Maggie O'Connell came rushing into Caroline's office, still clutching the carton of cigarettes she had gone down to the lobby to buy. "Caroline, I just saw Matthew and Joe walk into the lobby," she hissed.

"Are you sure?" As far as she knew, Matthew was out of town. His secretary had called Maggie on Wednesday, asking that she tell Mrs. Lyle that Mr. Lyle would be in Los Angeles until Sunday. Caroline wondered miserably if he had been with another woman, right here in Seattle, all along.

"I know he's supposed to be in L.A., but he's here. I ducked behind a pillar so they wouldn't see me, then took the next elevator."

What did they want? If they hadn't come directly to her office, where else would they go? Caroline grabbed her purse. "I think they came to talk to Sam. Maybe they found out about the payoffs."

She reached the outer office occupied by Sam Hanover's secretary to find the room vacant. The outer door had been closed, as was the door to Sam's private office. Even so, she could hear his voice and the voices of Matthew and Joe.

" . . . buried that stuff so deep that even a team of moles couldn't dig it out," Matthew drawled, his tone dripping sarcasm.

"I don't know what you're talking about," Sam retorted coolly.

"I'm talking about illegal payoffs, Hanover. I don't do business that way. I want your resignation on my desk by five o'clock this afternoon. You're off the payroll as of the thirtieth. I want you out of the building by Monday," Matthew ordered.

"Your imagination's been working overtime, Lyle. Nobody paid anybody any bribes," Sam answered.

Now Joe Symington took over with a detailed description of the irregularities he had uncovered, recited in a rapid staccato that did nothing to hide his disgust. "On government contracts, too, Hanover. The new S.E.C. commissioner will eat it up. He'll tell the U.S. Attorney to go for a one-way ticket to the Lompoc prison."

"I can share a room with your wife, Lyle" was the flippant response. "I wouldn't mind *that* at all."

Caroline winced. She couldn't believe that Matthew would tolerate such an insult, even if she bored him to distraction.

But he merely laughed, apparently amused by the comment.

The sound was like a dagger through Caroline's heart. She clutched at the doorjamb, too distraught to worry about whether the sound had carried inside. Then Sam was speaking again.

"Don't give me that, Lyle. You couldn't keep your eyes off her last Wednesday. You're not about to risk getting her embroiled in this. And you know that she was chairman, so she's just as culpable as I am."

There was a pause before Matthew's bland voice broke the silence. "The adoring husband. It made for a smooth acquisition, don't you agree?" When Sam made no reply, he continued, "Go ahead, Hanover. Pick up the phone. Call her. Ask her when the last time I touched her was."

"Matthew doesn't want any scandal attached to a company he just took over," Joe Symington put in. "You're lucky we're willing to let you out clean. But if you won't resign, we'll go public with this."

"You're not that tough, Lyle. Your wife . . ."

"You're right. I don't like the thought of my *ex*-wife in jail," Matthew broke in, "but if it's the price . . ."

His ex-wife? Caroline didn't wait to hear any more. She fled from the office and out of the building, not even stopping to tell Maggie that she was leaving for the day. Once she was behind the wheel of her car, she drove without thinking toward Hunt's Point, tears streaming down her face. Her most painful moments with Clay couldn't begin to compare with what she felt now.

She couldn't face Matthew. She needed some time alone, so that when they talked about a divorce she could pretend she was delighted to be getting out of the marriage. Zombielike, she threw some casual clothing into a suitcase and headed for Sea-Tac Airport.

She pulled into the airport garage feeling like a hunted animal. It didn't matter where she went. Matthew would find her. He would send Joe after her. He might not want her, but he would be angry when he found out that she had walked out on him. Women didn't do that to Matthew Lyle.

An outrageous inspiration came to her. She locked the car, hailed a taxi, and gave the driver an address in Clyde Hill. Joe Symington could find the proverbial needle in a haystack, but he would never think of searching his own home.

Janet was so distressed over Caroline's tear-streaked appearance that she hustled her into the house without a single word. She only asked what was wrong when both of them were seated in the kitchen.

Caroline burst into tears all over again. "I need a place to think. I don't want Matthew to find me."

"But here . . ."

"It's the last place he would look. Please, Janet. You said you would help," Caroline choked out.

Janet seemed to sense that Caroline was far too overwrought to offer explanations. "All right, Carrie," she said quietly. "You can stay in Lindsay's room. Joe hasn't set foot in there since last winter, ever since she started ranting about her privacy. She's at a girlfriend's tonight—I'll call her and tell her to spend the night there. She's a good girl—she'll keep her mouth shut."

Caroline was too upset to feel any relief. She couldn't eat and she couldn't sleep, and Janet wisely did not press her. She lay on Lindsay's bed, surrounded by records, clothing, cosmetics, and school papers, and tortured herself with thoughts of Matthew. Why had she ever met him? What was wrong with her, that no one had ever loved her? Was she a terrible person? A failure? How was she going to go on with her life, when she felt like she wanted to spend the rest of it hiding in bed?

When she heard Joe Symington walk up the stairs very late that night, her body stiffened in alarm. But he walked right past Lindsay's door to the end of the hall and the bedroom he shared with Janet.

He left early the next morning. Joey, who like his father had no idea that Caroline was even in the house, went over to the college library to study for finals. Only then did Janet go up to Lindsay's room, telling Caroline, "Joe spent most of last night at the airport, trying to track you down. He says that Matthew is out of his mind with worry. Are you sure you know what you're doing?"

Caroline managed a disconsolate nod. "He's not worried. Maybe his pride is injured because I left, but that's all. Believe me."

As before, Janet did not argue the point. She coaxed Caroline into taking a hot bath and brought her some tea and toast to eat when she came downstairs. Later, both women sat in the den, watching television.

The TV game shows helped keep Caroline's mind off Matthew, but also gave her a throbbing headache. Janet fetched her a glass of water and some aspirin, but insisted that what she really needed was a decent meal. Caroline declined. She knew she would be unable to keep a thing in her stomach.

But as the afternoon wore on and the initial shock of what she had overheard subsided, her common sense and courage reasserted themselves. "I think I could eat something, Janet," she announced. "And then I suppose I should go home. I'm only making myself sick by refusing to face up to things."

Janet patted her shoulder and led her back to the kitchen. Caroline managed to eat two soft-boiled eggs and was sipping some coffee when the front door opened. The sound of Joe and Matthew's voices made her start so violently that she nearly knocked over the cup.

Caroline heard the thud of booted feet against wood as one of them put his feet up on the coffee table. Janet went out to greet them. Though only a long common wall and an alcove separated the two rooms, the table where Caroline sat was not visible from the living room sofa. She heard Janet ask them if they wanted coffee and then two grunts, which she assumed were positive responses, before the other woman came back into the kitchen.

Then Matthew said impatiently, "Why did you drag me over here? Did you find Carrie?"

"You're really worried about her, aren't you, Matt? She'll turn up eventually," Joe replied nonchalantly.

"Damn it, I'll go insane if I have to wait for *eventually*, Joe. You know that!"

"Y'know, Matt," Joe drawled, "I kind of figured that when you fell, you'd fall hard. You're really nuts about her, aren't you?"

Caroline and Janet exchanged a look—Caroline bewildered, Janet smug—before the latter took the coffee back through to the living room. What was Joe Symington up to?

Caroline heard someone get up from the sofa; the sound of footsteps on the Persian carpet told her he was pacing back and forth. "Yes, I'm nuts about her!" Matthew exploded. "You know that I'm so in love with her that the last week has been torture! Are you going to tell me where in the bloody blazes she is so I can get this straightened out?"

"Yeah," his cousin said, surrounding the word with laughter. "*Now* I can tell you. I spent hours at Sea-Tac last night, shoving her picture under everyone's nose and trying to find out what plane she was on. Your wife is very beautiful, Matt . . . a very striking lady. She's the type that people notice."

"I know that, Joe, better than anyone. Get to the point." His voice wavered as he stalked around the room.

"About midnight, it finally occurred to me that she hadn't left the airport—at least not by plane. She parked her car there as a decoy, then came back into Seattle."

"Thank heaven." The pacing stopped and Caroline heard the sound of a body dropping heavily back onto the couch. "So did you find her?"

"I've spent all morning talking to taxi drivers. Do you know how many taxi drivers there are in Seattle, Matt?"

"You're enjoying this, aren't you?" Matthew accused. "You know exactly where my wife is, and you're sitting there taking your time telling me because you want to see me sweat. My own cousin!"

"Yeah, I admit I'm enjoying it." Joe laughed. "For the last ten years I've watched you whistle for any female you wanted, then wait until she fell into your bed. It's about time someone turned the tables."

There was a protracted silence. Finally Matthew spoke, his impatience not quite so evident. "Okay, Joe. I'm glad you've gotten a good laugh out of this. Anytime you're ready . . ."

"I found the cab driver, Matt. Would you believe that the guy turned out to be a stockholder in EBE? He not only recognized the picture, he knew who Carrie was. He said her face was puffy, like she'd been crying."

"Did he remember where he'd taken her?"

"Sure he remembered. Address in Clyde Hill. You want to take the upstairs or the downstairs?"

"She's *here?*" Matthew asked incredulously.

"That's right. She's here. I should put you over my knee, Janet. Here I've been chasing around Sea-Tac Airport half the night and talking to every cab driver in Seattle, and you have her hidden away in my own house!"

"I *knew* Carrie had things all mixed up," Janet said gleefully. "I finally outsmarted you! Oh, Joe, your face—it's precious. . . ."

Caroline got up from the table in a daze. Had she really heard that passionate declaration of love, that tormented concern? She walked out into the living room and stared at Matthew, shaking with apprehension. "You told Sam you were going to divorce me. You said . . ."

"You heard." Matthew wasn't asking a question, merely stating an obvious fact. "We figured that was why you took off." His gaze flickered to his cousin. "You knew she was listening. That's why you . . ."

"Never play poker against your husband, Carrie," Joe interrupted. "If you fell for the way he bluffed Sam, you'll lose every time."

"Bluffed?" Caroline repeated.

Matthew wasted no more time before taking her in his arms. At first, Caroline resisted, but there was such desperate relief in the way he hugged her that she had to believe the words she had overheard. Her arms went around his waist; she laid her head against his shoulder.

"Of course it was a bluff, Carrie," he murmured. "If Sam Hanover knew how much I love you, he would have been able to write his own ticket. I would do anything to protect you."

"I don't understand."

Matthew gently straightened, took Caroline's hand, and led her over to the sofa. Once they were seated he put his arm around her shoulder, as if seeking the comfort of physical contact. "It didn't take us over a week to find out about the payoffs Sam made. We were sure of that by Saturday night. What took so much time was uncovering the opposite."

"The opposite?" Janet chimed in. "You mean he was on the take?"

"A complicated scheme of falsified expenditures and kickbacks. Your jamming system is the best in the field, Carrie. He didn't need to bribe anyone to get those contracts. He and his pals were lining their own wallets," Joe explained. "We figure that Clay Spencer's death provided too good an opportunity to resist."

"You mean Clay had nothing to do with the payoffs?" Caroline asked.

Joe shook his head. "It was Hanover's baby all the way. My guess is that he first got the idea when Clay was dying, but he was shrewd enough to wait until you actually took over. You were new and inexperienced, and he wanted you legally implicated, just in case he needed to use a little blackmail. I had to strong-arm my contacts in four different companies to put together what happened. Bribery isn't something that most people want to talk about, and the other companies have some housecleaning of their own to do. It didn't suit our purpose to let Hanover know we were aware of the whole story. We can't prove anything without a major S.E.C. investigation, and none of the companies involved want that. My guess is that your late controller has a lot of cash socked away in a Swiss bank account."

"He was faced with a choice, sweetheart," Matthew added. "He could take the risk that I was bluffing and find out if I'd really be willing to risk getting you involved. Or he could content himself with what he'd managed to steal. He didn't want to resign as controller—he likes the prestige, the social recognition, and the salary. But it wasn't worth sticking his neck out for those things when he'll draw a sizable pension. I typed his resignation letter and had him sign it. Officially, he's taking an early retirement for health reasons. Hanover's no fool; he has nothing to gain by making trouble. I sent him off to Europe for a few weeks."

"But what happens when he comes back?" Caroline asked. "We won't be divorced. How can you be sure he won't say anything?"

Matthew shrugged. "What for? He won't be able to get his old job back. It will be filled. But if he makes any accusations, Joe and I will look at him like he's playing with half a deck. We never found anything irregular in those books, did we, Joe?"

"Clean as a whistle," Joe winked.

"Who's going to corroborate his story? The guys who paid him off? The ones who took his money?" Matthew asked pointedly. "He'll take it philosophically, believe me." He took Caroline by the hand and led her out to his car, taking her into his arms when both of them were seated inside. "You've got a very devious mind, Mrs. Lyle," he said. "It's not everyone who outwits me and my cousin, even for twenty-four hours." Then he bent his head for a passionate, lingering kiss that left both of them hungry for more complete satisfaction.

"Let's go home, Matthew," she breathed.

He released her reluctantly and started the car. As they drove, Caroline asked, "Why didn't you tell me what you were up to?"

"Why didn't *you* tell *me* about Sam Hanover? I think

that's more to the point, Caroline," he said very sternly. It was the first time she could remember hearing him use her full name.

"I couldn't. I was hoping you would never find out. I was afraid that you—well, that you . . ." The accusation was so dreadful that Caroline couldn't bring herself to finish the sentence.

"You *should* be embarrassed!" Matthew scolded. "What kind of a guy do you think I am?"

"A ruthless, tough business tycoon who can be sweet and gentle and *very* sexy. And who I happen to love to distraction," Caroline said softly.

Matthew's eyes swung from the road. "Since when?" he demanded.

"I don't know, and watch where you're going, darling. Maybe since the moment we met, and I spilled soda all over your jacket. Or since the night I got sick in the San Juans. I knew I loved you the night I told you about Clay, after we made love. But you still haven't explained why you didn't tell me you were going to swipe my company records."

"First, because I didn't trust you. The night I proposed, I could tell you were terrified about something in those books. There had to be some sort of fraud, and I didn't want to believe you were directly involved. I was hoping you would tell me yourself, but when you didn't, I decided maybe it was just as well. I was afraid that if I told you what I was going to do you would run to Hanover in a panic and he would manage to conveniently misplace half the files. I wanted the guy out, not hanging over both our heads."

"But how did you know it was Sam? And why didn't you tell me afterward why you'd taken everything?"

"He was the logical suspect. I knew he ran the company until Clay's death. That meant he had both the access and the contacts. And when he wasn't at the wedding, I was certain he was the guy we wanted. As for why I didn't tell you . . ." Matthew parked the car in front of the house and turned off the ignition. "Let's go inside, sweetheart."

Once they were seated in the living room, Matthew continued, "Don't think it didn't hurt, Carrie. I've never spent a more painful week. Do you remember the way I made love to you the night before Joe and I came to your office?"

Caroline nodded, recalling the wild domination of Matthew's caresses.

"I wasn't going to touch you that night, but I couldn't stop myself when I found you awake in bed. In twelve hours you were going to hate my guts, and it tore me apart. I guess what happened was an animal urge to mark my territory." He paused. "Did I hurt you, Carrie?"

"You upset me. It was also . . . exciting," she admitted with a hot blush. "But why were you so cool all week?"

"I couldn't think of any other way to protect you. I knew the first thing Hanover would say was that I cared too much to risk hurting you. I needed to convince him that I *didn't* care, and that meant convincing *you*. As it turned out, he didn't call my bluff—didn't drag you down to his office and start asking questions. But he might have. I had to make sure he would believe you if you told him things were finished between us. I've already noticed that you're a rotten liar."

"The things you said to Sam just about destroyed me," Caroline admitted, nestling into the crook of his arm. "I was so in love with you, and it seemed like you didn't care at all. I really thought you were telling the truth—that you weren't interested anymore."

"I love you, Carrie. Never doubt that," was the tender response. "But you didn't make it easy. It took me a week to cool down after that disaster in the San Juans. I had myself convinced that you were a manipulative little gold digger who had maneuvered Spencer into marrying you. But too many things didn't fit. It wasn't just Joe and Janet. You were too vulnerable, too afraid of being hurt. I couldn't believe you were acting. I suppose I was in love with you before we got married, but I couldn't really accept my own feelings until the night you told me about your childhood and about your marriage to Spencer."

He got up from the couch and disappeared into the kitchen, returning with a bottle of chilled white wine and two glasses. "Want some?" he asked.

As Caroline sipped, he continued, "As long as I'm baring my soul, I might as well admit that when Joe first brought your company to my attention, I wasn't all that interested. In the present economy, we're focusing on consolidation, not further acquisitions. We acquired some stock and kept on top of what was happening. Then I began to hear about the icy Caroline McKay Spencer. It intrigued me. Someone showed me your picture and told me about your nickname. At that point, I decided I wanted to meet you. But on my terms."

"You were a beast to keep avoiding me that way," Caroline pouted.

"I'd heard that you were a tough lady to deal with. I decided that it would help to have the element of surprise on my side. I never expected you to walk right into the trap I set with that game of pretending you were someone else."

"It was a fantasy. I thought you were the most gorgeous man I'd ever laid eyes on when I saw you at

187

the boat show. No one had ever affected me that way before. I wanted to pretend we were two other people, not enemies in a proxy fight. After we actually went out, I never managed to get my defenses in place again." Caroline took his glass out of his hand and set it on the end table. She ran her fingers down his jaw.

"Fortunately for me," Matthew said, nuzzling her neck. "I've had a rocky time with you as it is." His lips brushed her mouth. "I'm going to split your company, Mrs. Lyle. With a little help and an end to certain fraudulent practices, I think your nonmilitary products will do very well."

It was difficult for Caroline to concentrate on what he was saying, given the fact that his hand had wandered underneath her shirt and was lightly stroking her breasts.

"You going to stick around to manage things for me, sweetheart?" he asked.

"I don't—I made a mess of everything, Matthew, not knowing what Sam was doing," she answered rather breathlessly.

"You were new. He took advantage of that. It wouldn't happen now." His tongue darted to her ear, tracing the outline of her earlobe.

"Uh—then yes." Caroline twisted her head so that her lips intercepted his wandering tongue. After several teasing forays at her mouth, he began to kiss her in earnest, his probing, languorous exploration arousing her until she was all but begging him to love her again.

"Upstairs, I think," he mumbled hoarsely, picking her up. As he carried her into the bedroom, Caroline whispered into his ear, "Do you think I could have a vacation early next spring, darling?"

"Umm. What happens next spring?"

"Your mother thinks I'm impossibly liberated. She disapproves . . ."

"I don't care *what* she thinks," Matthew interrupted. "I like you the way you are."

"Still," Caroline persisted, "we could give her a little something to make her happy."

Matthew laughed as he tossed her onto the bed. "I'm not about to object. I like the idea. Just think—our son could be the next Bill Bradley," he mused. "College All-American, Rhodes scholar, pro basketball player, United States senator. We've got all the right genes, sweetheart."

"Really?" Caroline asked with feigned coolness. "And suppose we have a girl, you male chauvinist! Your mother wants a granddaughter, you know!"

"Carrie, my beloved, enough is enough. I'll only accept so much liberation from the women in my family, and that's it! A corporation president for a wife is one thing, but no daughter of mine is going to make it her life's goal to get drafted by the Seattle SuperSonics!"

"How about senator from the state of Washington?" Caroline countered.

"If you don't shut up and let me get you where you belong, there won't be any offspring, Mrs. Lyle."

"Who's talking?" Caroline giggled and held out her arms to him.

Silhouette Romance

15-Day Free Trial Offer
6 Silhouette Romances

6 Silhouette Romances, free for 15 days! We'll send you 6 new Silhouette Romances to keep for 15 days, absolutely free! If you decide not to keep them, send them back to us. You pay nothing.

Free Home Delivery. But if you enjoy them as much as we think you will, keep them by paying the invoice enclosed with your free trial shipment. We'll pay all shipping and handling charges. You get the convenience of Home Delivery and we pay the postage and handling charge each month.

Don't miss a copy. The Silhouette Book Club is the way to make sure you'll be able to receive every new romance we publish before they're sold out. There is no minimum number of books to buy and you can cancel at any time.

This offer expires February 28, 1982

Silhouette Book Club, Dept. **SBG**17B
120 Brighton Road, Clifton, NJ 07012

Please send me 6 Silhouette Romances to keep for 15 days, absolutely free. I understand I am not obligated to join the Silhouette Book Club unless I decide to keep them.

NAME_____

ADDRESS_____

CITY_____STATE_____ZIP_____

IT'S YOUR OWN SPECIAL TIME

Contemporary romances for today's women.
Each month, six very special love stories will be yours
from SILHOUETTE.
Look for them wherever books are sold
or order now from the coupon below.

$1.50 each

Silhouette Romance

SILHOUETTE BOOKS, Department SB/1
1230 Avenue of the Americas
New York, NY 10020

Please send me the books I have checked above. I am enclosing
$_____ (please add 50¢ to cover postage and handling. NYS and
NYC residents please add appropriate sales tax). Send check or
money order—no cash or C.O.D.'s please. Allow six weeks for delivery.

NAME_____

ADDRESS_____

CITY_____STATE/ZIP_____